Future Faces of Food
and Food Security

Also from Westphalia Press

westphaliapress.org

Future Faces of Food and Food Security

Volume 2, Number 2 / Volume 3, Number 1
of World Food Policy

Edited by Keokam Kraisoraphong

WESTPHALIA PRESS
An imprint of Policy Studies Organization

Future Faces of Food and Food Security:
Volume 2, Number 2 / Volume 3, Number 1 of World Food Policy
All Rights Reserved © 2016 by Policy Studies Organization

Westphalia Press
An imprint of Policy Studies Organization
1527 New Hampshire Ave., NW
Washington, D.C. 20036
info@ipsonet.org

ISBN-13: 978-1-63391-730-9
ISBN-10: 1633917304

Cover design by Jeffrey Barnes:
www.jbarnesbook.design

Daniel Gutierrez-Sandoval, Executive Director
PSO and Westphalia Press

Updated material and comments on this edition
can be found at the Westphalia Press website:
www.westphaliapress.org

Volume 2, Issue 2/Volume 3, Issue 1, Fall 2015/Spring 2016
©2016 Policy Studies Organization

Table of Contents

WORLD FOOD POLICY — A Journal of the PSO in collaboration with the Royal Institute of Thailand

A Journal of the PSO in collaboration with the Royal Institute of Thailand

Editorial: Welcome to *World Food Policy*

This double issue of *World Food Policy* (*WFP*) brings together articles submitted for the World Food Policy Conference, held in Bangkok during December 17-18, 2015 in celebration of Her Royal Highness Princess Maha Chakri Sirindhorn's 60th Birthday Anniversary.

Organized under the theme *Future Faces of Food and Farming: Regional Challenges*, the Conference aimed to provide a forum for in-depth discussions and perspective sharing on key topics important to world food policy. It emphasized the crucial role that research and knowledge exchange within and between academic and policy circles play in understanding multi-faceted challenges of food and food security, and in providing guidance that can help us – collectively, regionally and globally – address pressing policy questions related to food production and sustainability.

The articles in this issue are listed by the topics of fisheries, fresh markets, food security and income diversification. Also included are short articles from the Conference keynote speech as well as those from the roundtable discussions on *Food Security in an Age of Falling Commodity and Food Prices* – held during the Conference.

A book, *Signpost of Learning*, that collects His Majesty King Bhumibol's experiments and pilot projects on small-scale agriculture, food production, and sufficiency economy was published by Westphalian Press of the Policy Studies Organization (PSO) for the occasion and launched at the conference. Along with a number of presentations by selected conference participants, the book has been made accessible at the *WFP* website: http://www.ipsonet.org/publications/open-access/world-food-policy – so that valuable lessons learned from the book and the Royal Projects will contribute to the repertoire of best practices and body of knowledge which can be applied, adapted and extended.

The 2015 World Food Policy Conference, which has provided the contents for this double issue was jointly organized by the Royal Society of Thailand (RST) and the Policy Studies Organization (PSO), with the financial support from the National Research Council of Thailand (NRCT) and the National Food Institute (NFI) of Thailand's Ministry of Industry.

doi: 10.18278/wfp.2.2.3.1.1

Call for Papers

W_orld Food Policy_ (**WFP**) editors invite submission of manuscripts contributing to the Journal's Aim and Scope: to promote a multi-disciplinary forum for generating the analysis and understanding of global trends – as well as regional and local forces shaping food and food policies around the world.

More than ever before, the world now faces paradoxes and predicaments on the problems related to food. On the one hand, we have problems of mulnutrition, hunger, and falling prices of commodities and agricultural products. On the other hand, we also have to deal with rising costs of obesity-related health problems, food waste, and increasing corporate monopolies of seeds and medicines through patents. Several long-term trends also contribute to future uncertainties that call for urgent international policy collaboration and transnational adjustments at all levels to address conditions critical to food sustainability and security: climate change, deforestation, rising world population, aging societies, depletion of freshwater resources, to name but a few.

For further information on the journal's aim and scope please consult **WFP** website: http://www.ipsonet.org/publications/open-access/world-food-policy

WFP is a scholarly, peer-reviewed, multi-disciplinary journal of the Policy Studies Organization (PSO), Washington DC - a nonprofit society founded as an outgrowth of the American Political Science Association for those in a variety of fields who were interested in how public policy and organizational policy were being studied and discussed. Based on the concern that policies should be informed policies and that research knowledge must be effectively disseminated to reach those who actually set policies, the PSO seeks to disseminate scholarship and information to serve those making and evaluating policy.

WFP's board of editors comprises those nominated from a broad diversity of institutions and countries, and are acknowledged by the Royal Society of Thailand (RST), the journal's host institution: http://www.ipsonet.org/images/WFP/WFP_Editorial_Biographies_2015.pdf

All manuscripts should be submitted electronically as an email attachment, and addressed to the editor-in-chief at: WFP.editorial@gmail.com

For details on Manuscript Preparation and Manuscript Submission please consult **WFP** Author Guidelines at: http://www.ipsonet.org/images/WFP/Author_Guidelines_2015.pdf

Food Security in Rural Cambodia and Fishing in the Mekong in the Light of Declining Fish Stocks

Rebecca Hartje[A], Dorothee Bühler[A] & Ulrike Grote[A]

Fishing in the Mekong River is of utmost importance for rural livelihoods in parts of Cambodia. As a result of ecosystem changes, fish stocks are expected to decline. Using data on 600 rural households collected in two waves in 2013 and 2014 in the province of Stung Treng, we assess the current situation of food security in relation to fishing. To proxy food security, we consider energy and protein intakes as well as Food Security Indexes. Quantitative results show that fishing households had a more nutritious diet in the past week, are more engaged in subsistence activities and had lower additional food expenditure. Furthermore, fishing is effective in reducing seasonal food insecurity for households in the lowest income quartile. In the light of declining fish stocks these findings underscore the need for fishing households to adjust their income earning activities to the expected changes. We call for policymakers to account for the most fish-dependent groups of the population when designing or adjusting development policies for the area that could potentially affect fish stocks.

Keywords: Cambodia, Fishing, Mekong River, Nutrition, Food Security Indicators

Introduction

Fish is without doubt the second most important food next to rice in Cambodia. As much as 75% to 79% of the annual consumption of animal protein is supplied by fish and as many as 39% of Cambodian households have at least one member engaged in fishing (Ahmed et al. 1998; Israel et al. 2007). According to Baran (2005), Cambodia is the most intensive inland fishery in the world with ~20 kg of fish per capita caught annually. The majority of Cambodian fishers are engaged in small- to medium-scale fisheries which supply the largest part of the annual catch volume (Van Zalinge et al. 2000). Along with the importance of fish, agriculture remains the most significant source of income in rural Cambodia. In this context fishing can be viewed as a means of diversification to reduce risk or mitigate the impact of crop failure (Baran 2005; Smith, Nguyen Khoa, and Lorenzen 2005). Besides its cultural importance and influence on

[A] Institute for Environmental Economics and World Trade, Leibniz Universität Hannover, Germany.

doi: 10.18278/wfp.2.2.3.1.2

people's subjective well-being (Bush 2004; Marschke and Berkes 2006), it plays an essential role in ensuring food security in many rural households not only through fish consumption but also through cash income from selling fish. More than 50% of the small-scale fishers' catch is sold (Hori et al. 2006; Navy and Bhattarai 2009). Fish is an ideal food to improve food security in developing countries such as Cambodia because, despite access regulations, it is easily accessible even for poor households and it has a high density of proteins and micronutrients (Kawarazuka and Béné 2010; 2011).

Although the livelihood outcomes[2] of many rural Cambodians depend on small-scale capture fisheries, the output from aquaculture still remains low (Hortle, Lieng, and Valbo-Jorgensen 2004; Hortle 2007; Navy and Bhattarai 2009). At the same time, aquaculture is undertaken by only a limited number of households in the area (Bush 2004). After the end of political unrest in the 1990s Cambodia's fishing output increased. There is an academic debate whether fish stocks are currently declining (Hortle, Lieng, and Valbo-Jorgensen 2004; Baran, Jantunen, and Chong 2007). Most current empirical evidence points at a negative development of fish stocks in the Mekong River, especially in important migratory species which contribute significantly to the catch in the study site of this article (Roberts and Baird 1995;

Baran and Myschowoda 2009; Orr et al. 2012). However, even if fish stocks were currently not declining, reduction in the near future seems to be certain (Baran and Myschowoda 2008). Declining fishing margins are already observed because costs increase and output per fishing trip decreases (Navy and Bhattarai 2009). There is a number of reasons for the reduction of fish stocks, among them are the construction of hydroelectric dams in the upstream countries of the Mekong River, habitat loss, overfishing due to improved technology, increasing population, and illegal fishing practices (Hortle, Lieng, and Valbo-Jorgensen 2004; Hori et al. 2006; Baran, Jantunen, and Chong 2007; Navy and Bhattarai 2009). The active management of fish resources and enforcement of fishing regulations is important to sustain the extraordinary productivity of Cambodian fisheries (Degen and Thuok 1998). However, these measures may prove to be useless if the construction of further dams for hydropower as well as for water regulation and irrigation leads to artificial changes in water levels and barring of fish-spawning grounds resulting in a reduction of fishing output (Hortle, Lieng, and Valbo-Jorgensen 2004; Ziv et al. 2012).

Part of the narrative of decreasing fish stocks in the Mekong river is the fear that the decline will lead to reduced food security (Arthur and Friend 2011).

---

[1] The concept of livelihoods is extensive and refers to more than what is the focus of this article. We refer to the term of livelihood to point at the importance of fishing among the wide portfolio of livelihood activities undertaken by the rural households to earn a living. While in theory livelihood outcomes include various results of these activities for a household, we focus on food security as it is the main point of concern in this article.

Considering the high dependency of livelihood outcomes on fishing, the good nutritious value of fish (Kawarazuka and Béné 2010), and the fact that fishers often consume the fish they have caught (Ahmed et al. 1999; Gomna and Rana 2007) it appears to be clear that a reduction in fish stocks will have a negative impact on households' food security. Still, so far the potential impact has not been quantified (Pukinskis and Geheb 2012). Furthermore, not all households will be affected in a similar way. While fishing for cash income and household consumption is pursued equally across all socioeconomic groups in the lower Mekong river basin (Garaway 2005), declining fish stocks may have different effects on individual household's diets depending on their socioeconomic status and the portfolio of their livelihood activities, especially if they are fishers. The importance of fish for nutrition in the overall population undeniable (Bezerra da Costa, Dinyz de Melo, and Macedo Lopes 2014; Dey et al. 2005), and especially fishers are expected to be relatively more affected by declining fish stocks. However, this relationship has also not been quantified yet.

More affluent fishing households have got resources such as human capital, cash income, and physical assets to shift their income earning and subsistence activities away from fishing when fish stocks decline, for example, by investing in irrigation systems or aquaculture (Bush 2004). By investing in new sources of income, these affluent households can hence adapt to the new situation and replace foregone income from fishing. Meanwhile, poorer[2] fishing households may simply not have enough income and assets to invest and adapt, leaving them exposed to the losses of fishing income. Furthermore, Nguyen et al. (2015) show for Cambodia that richer households extract absolutely more natural resources than poorer households. Yet, the share of natural resource extraction in total income is higher in poorer households than in richer ones, making the poor households more dependent on natural resources. As a large share of the natural resource income in Cambodia originates from fishing, it implies that poorer households depend more on fishing in terms of income than more affluent ones. When these households depend more on fishing income and have less resources to adopt new income sources, their food security could be more affected by declining fish stocks than that of better-off households.

Additionally, even though fishing takes place across all socioeconomic groups, fish may be overall more important in the diet of poorer fishing households as they have got less access to other sources of animal protein than richer households (Kawarazuka and Béné 2010). Households which earn their living from subsistence activities, such as agriculture and fishing, may face greater difficulty in shifting to other sources of animal protein in their diets than households

---

[2] With the term "poor" we do not refer to households which are absolutely poor as defined by a cut-off point but we mean households that are less affluent than others according to the distribution of incomes, that is, the lowest income quartile.

which use fishing to supplement their income from off-farm employment and businesses. This is because in the latter case there is a larger cash flow which can be quickly redistributed away from other consumption to buy meat or fish whereas in the former households will have to shift their agricultural portfolio to cash crops for buying fish and meat or to more livestock and aquaculture production as sources of animal protein. These adjustments again need investments.

The importance of fishing in Cambodia, the expected decline of fish stocks in the Mekong River and its potential impact on households' food security depending on the socioeconomic status and whether they are fishers leads us to a number of questions: How much do fishing activities actually influence the diets of fishers in comparison to non-fishers? Is fish of greater importance in the food security of poorer fishing households than in others? What are the other typical income-earning strategies of households that fish, that is, how can they be characterized? We want to quantify the effects of fishing activities on fish consumption, nutrition and food security by comparing rural households engaged in small-scale fishing to households which do not fish. By doing so we can proxy for the impact of missing fishing income on fishing households' food security. Furthermore, we test the hypothesis whether poorer fishing households rely most on fish in terms of food security and nutrients. By analyzing income-earning strategies which are typically adopted by fishing households we can characterize those households which will be most affected by a further decline in fish stocks. Food security at the

household level is a very broad concept that relates to nutrition and its stability over time. Specifically, we measure protein and caloric intakes as well as the Food Consumption Score (FCS) which indicates dietary diversity and weighs food groups according to their importance in terms of adequate nutrition. The FCS has been validated to measure household food security (Wiesmann et al. 2009). Furthermore, we utilize the Household Food Insecurity Access Scale (HFIAS), the Coping Strategies Index (CSI) and the reduced Coping Strategies Index (rCSI) to proxy food security.

Our article uses a novel panel dataset representative of the rural population of Stung Treng collected in spring 2013 and 2014. We quantify the interrelations between fishing and fish consumption in the lower Mekong river basin for the first time and identify the typical economic activities of fishers. We add to the existing literature of fish and food security (Bezerra da Costa, Dinyz de Melo, and Macedo Lopes 2014; Dey et al. 2005; Lam et al. 2012; Ziv et al. 2012) by exploring the importance of fish for different types of households, namely fishing- and non-fishing households in the whole sample, and the poorest income quantile. With this we want to increase our understanding of who will be most affected by the predicted changes in the Mekong river's ecosystem and how wide the potential gap in nutrition could be that needs to be filled with activities which replace fishing income. Thorough comprehension of the links between changes in the river's ecosystem, the economic activities of small-scale fisheries and household nutrition may help policymakers and development practitioners channel the present transformation of the rural economy to better outcomes for those who are most vulnerable to these changes. Beyond the scope of the lower Mekong river basin, this knowledge may also improve our understanding of transformation processes in other areas where livelihood outcomes, especially food security, are highly dependent on small-scale fresh water fishery such as in the floodplains of Bangladesh (Sultana and Thompson 2007), in Myanmar (FAO 2003), or lake Victoria in Africa (Matsuishi et al. 2006).

The remainder of the article is structured as follows: The section "Sample and Methodology" describes the dataset and how food security and nutrition are measured. The next section "Results" introduces and discusses the results. The last section concludes.

Sample and methodology

Data

We collected the data in two household surveys in May 2013 and 2014 in the Cambodian province of Stung Treng. The original sample from 2013 contained 600 households which we identified in a two-stage sampling procedure. In the first step, 30 villages were sampled from the list of all 129 rural villages in the province with probabilities proportional to their size (PPS) measured as the number of households. In the second step, 20 households were randomly sampled from each village's household list. This procedure results in equal probability for each household in the province to be part of the sample and is based on

the procedures described in Hardeweg, Klasen, and Waibel (2013) and United Nations (2008). Due to attrition 11 households were dropped from the sample, another 26 observations had to be dropped as outliers.

We used two different questionnaires during the household survey: one long household questionnaire and a shorter village questionnaire. The former was administered to the household head and the person in charge of decisions about food eaten by the household. While the household head can be male or female, the person making decisions about food is usually a female household member. The latter questionnaire was answered by the village head or deputy village head. The main household questionnaire usually refers to the period of the past twelve months and covers basic data on individual household members, sections on all possible income components, such as agriculture and fishing, information on assets, land and consumption. Furthermore, a comprehensive food security section measuring for example household dietary diversity, FCS and calorie and protein intake was applied using the 1-week recall method. Additionally, to capture periods of food insecurity across the past year, other indicators such as months of adequate food provisioning, CSI and FCS for different seasons were measured with a 1-year recall section.

In comparison to data from other sources, our sample is representative of the rural population of Stung Treng. As depicted in Table B1 in Appendix B, the average household size is 5.22, which is close to the figure provided by the NCDD (2009) for the province of Stung Treng.

The household heads are on average 45 years old, 12% of them are female, and 63% of all household heads report to be literate. This is close to the figure of 65% literacy in the 25-60 year old population reported by NCDD (2009). 82% of all households are ethnic Khmers. Other important ethnic groups are Kuoy (10%), Lao (3%), and Kavet (3%). Fishing is common in all ethnic groups. Most households are engaged in some kind of subsistence agriculture with lowland rainfed rice being the most widespread subsistence crop and the main staple. Besides rice, fruits are other important subsistence crops in terms of the number of households growing them; however, the quantity of fruits produced by each household is low. Irrigation and more than one rice harvest per year is extremely rare. Important cash crops are cassava and rice. Natural resource extraction, such as fishing, hunting, collecting, or logging, is another common source of income, along with family-run small businesses, most of them without external employees, and wage employment, for example as a government official or farm laborer. Labor migration is rare and there are no large-scale companies which provide employment in the province. Further information on this dataset can be found in Bühler et al. (2015).

The household survey was administered in Khmer by a mixed-gender team of 15 enumerators. All of them had previous experience in socioeconomic household surveys and were trained during lectures, field days, and role plays for 1 week before starting the survey. About two thirds of the team was from the capital Phnom Penh, the rest was recruited locally in the province of Stung Treng. In the following we use the data from both survey waves by pooling them.

As livelihood activities and their outcomes are closely connected to the natural cycles of the year in the rhythm of the dry and rainy season in the area of Stung Treng, a household's food security may change depending on the season. We collected the data during the end of the open fishing season (Navy and Bhattarai 2009) which takes place just before the rainy season starts and water levels rise, that is, data on the past week falls in this season. Food security during other seasons was captured by asking specifically for the situation in the past year's planting, pre-harvest and post-harvest seasons with the main staple crop, lowland rainfed rice, being the crop of reference. To capture specific events of food insecurity we also asked for the situation in the worst week and worst month in the past year, according to the subjective impression of the household.

Measuring Food Security

Today's most commonly used definition of food security was adopted at the World Food Summit in 1996. Accordingly "*Food security exists when all people, at all times, have physical, [social][3] and economic access to sufficient safe and nutritious food that meets their dietary needs and food preferences for an active and healthy life*" (FAO 1996). Based

---

[3] The term "social" was added in 2002.

on the definition, the following four dimensions of food security are derived: (i) availability–relates to the actual disposability of food; (ii) access–refers to households' ability to acquire food in sufficient quality and quantity; (iii) use and utilization–captures behavioral, health and hygiene components; and (iv) stability–covers the temporal aspect of food security, that is, seasonal income or output fluctuations which should ideally not affect food security.

There is a range of indicators which attempt to measure the different dimensions of food security at the household level. However, as Maxwell, Vaitla, and Coates (2014) point out, the picture changes quite substantially depending on the respective indicator looked at. This is why we analyze the FCS, the Household Food Insecurity Access Score (HFIAS), the (reduced) Coping Strategies Index (CSI and rCSI)[4], caloric intake, and protein intake in parallel to proxy food security. The FCS, calorie and protein intakes measure all foods consumed by the household in the past week, regardless whether they are consumed during family meals or in between the main meals. The HFIAS and (r)CSI measures refer to the worst month of the past year (according to the subjective impression of the household) and additionally we asked the households to recall the food they have typically eaten in a week in the pre-rice-harvest, post-rice-harvest, rice planting season, and the worst week of the past 12 months. For a detailed description of the construction

of the different indicators please refer to Appendix A.

The FCS asks about how often certain food groups were eaten by the household in the past week. To construct the score, the frequency of each food groups is weighted by a score according to its nutritious value and all resulting figures are summed up. The FCS belongs to measures of dietary diversity which have been found to indicate diet's micronutrient adequacy (Hatløy, Torheim, and Oshaug 1998; Steyn et al. 2006). Evidence shows that it is a valid measure of the food security access dimension (Christiaensen, Boisvert and Hoddinott 2000b; Wiesmann et al. 2009; Maxwell, Vaitla, and Coates 2014) even across different cultures (Melgar-Quinonez et al. 2006). Similar to the FCS, the HFIAS measures the prevalence of household food insecurity in terms of access (Coates, Swindale, and Bilinsky 2007). In contrast to dietary diversity measures this indicator draws on the idea that households who experience food insecurity will engage in predictable reactions which can be measured and quantified in a survey and displayed in a scale. In addition, the (r)CSI measures household behavior observed in times of food shortage and therewith captures coping strategies used to manage food shortage (Maxwell and Caldwell 2008). While all of the indicators are in principle capable of shedding light on the availability and access aspect of food security (Maxwell et al. 1999; Christiaensen and Boisvert 2000; Ruel

---

[4] The CSI is a context specific indicator using a broader range of questions whereas the rCSI is based on questions addressing behaviors found to be frequently applied across countries.

2002; Wiesmann et al. 2009; Deitchler et al. 2011; Headey and Ecker 2013), the caloric and protein intakes additionally allow to refer to the health situation within the household (De Haen, Klasen, and Qaim 2011; Headey and Ecker 2013). The dimension of stability is partly captured by considering the FCS across different seasons. The utilization dimension of food security is the only one we cannot address with these indicators.

Testing for differences in mean

In the analysis *t* tests are used to compare the descriptive statistics of fishers to non-fishers. Due to the high number of observations, a normal distribution of all variables can be assumed. Different specifications, such as Welch's *t* tests for unequal variances, lead to very similar results.

Results

Fishing in Stung Treng

In 2013 we recorded 372 different fishing activities across all 600 households in the sample. Out of these, 295 activities were reported to take place in the river, 45 in a stream or canal, and 15 in a fish pond. The targets of these fishing activities are usually all kinds of fish species, whether they are small or large. There are open (October–May) and closed (June–September) fishing seasons and other access regulations, but small-scale fishing for household use is always possible. The return to fishing changes a lot depending on the season (Navy and Bhattarai 2009). About 25% of the households in the sample report to fish on > 180 days in the year, but for most households fishing remains to be a

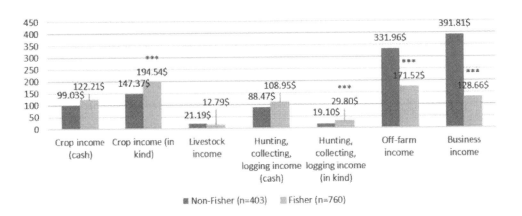

Figure 1: Comparison of mean annual per capita income from different sources between fishers and non-fishers in Stung Treng, Cambodia. All values are monetary values in terms of 2005 PPP \$. Two-sided t tests for different variable means between fishers and non-fishers, pooled sample 2013 and 2014. Significance Levels: *$p<0.1$, **$p<0.05$, ***$p<0.01$

seasonal activity. Fishers who report to go fishing year-round have got lower average yields per trip than seasonal fishers. The average total annual catch among fishing households is estimated to be around 314 kg. Slightly more than half of this amount is reported to be consumed by the households, the rest is sold. Only one of the households in our sample reports to be engaged in aquaculture.

With regard to household characteristics fishing households are on average larger than non-fishing households and they are less often headed by females. Fishers have got lower incomes than non-fishers; however, fishing is well-distributed across the whole income distribution (Figure B1 in Appendix B). While there are no significant differences in the production and consumption of livestock, fishers have significantly lower additional annual food expenditure per capita than non-fishers. More details on these figures may be found in Appendix B.

Figure 1 depicts the most important income sources in the sample and compares the income from these sources between fishers and non-fishers. It becomes apparent that fishing households have significantly more income from subsistence activities than non-fishing households because their in-kind income from crops and hunting is higher. This finding matches the observation from above that the additional annual food expenditure is significantly lower for fishers than for non-fishers. Meanwhile, non-fishing households have significantly more income from business and off-farm employment which is mostly cash income.

Fishing and Food Security

Figure 2 compares nutrition and food security indicators of the whole sample, fishers and non-fishers and tests the difference between fishers and non-fishers in two-sided mean comparison tests. The mean caloric intake in the sample accounting for adult equivalents is 2180 kcal per capita per day. Daily per capita protein intake is on average 78 grams. Roughly 40% of the total daily proteins and 20% of total calories come from eating fish. Even though the FCS only categorizes 10.6% of the overall households in our sample as food insecure at thresholds adjusted for high sugar consumption (World Food Programme 2008), 30% of the households consume <1800 kcal per adult equivalent per day, a common threshold for undernutrition (Svedberg 2002). Given that Lovon and Mathiassen (2014) find that judgment on food security in terms of adequate food consumption according to FCS cut-off points generally underestimates energy deficiency these different findings are not surprising. The average FCS for the whole sample is just >53 points. The comparison of fishers versus non-fishers in the whole sample generally shows that fishing households take in significantly more calories and proteins per capita per day. The same is true for calories and proteins from fish. This difference in nutrition variables between fishers and non-fishers is confirmed by the significant differences in the overall FCSs for the past week.

Table 1 depicts the make-up of the FCSs for the whole sample as well as for fishers and non-fishers. It uses two-sided mean comparison tests to assess the statistical significance of the

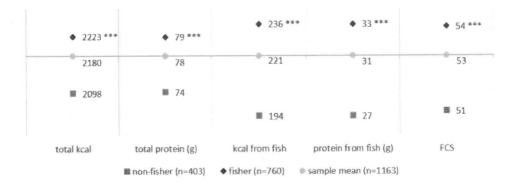

Figure 2: Comparison of Nutrition Indicators in the past week between whole sample, fishers and non-fishers in Stung Treng, Cambodia. Two-sided t tests were used for different variable means between fishers and non-fishers, pooled sample 2013 and 2014. Significance Levels: $*p<0.1$, $**p<0.05$, $***p<0.01$. Depicted data points are standardized around their mean. Kilocalories and Proteins are calculated as per capita in adult equivalents

differences. Looking at the different components of the FCS in the whole sample gives an idea about the relative importance of different foods. According to the average FCS across all households, staples are eaten daily in nearly every household. This is complemented by animal proteins on ~5.5 days in the week[5] in the average household. Out of these, fish is eaten on ~4 days as can be seen from the FCSs from total animal protein and fish. The FCSs from vegetables and fruits[6] are low, which is typical of the average Cambodian diet. Looking at the make-up of the FCS also sheds light upon the potential impact of changes in the availability of fish on the total FCS. As the average weekly score of 54 points in fishing households contains ~17.5 points from fish, the disappearance of fish from the diet would let the average fishing household drop below the threshold to a borderline diet[7] and hence into the food insecure area of the FCS. However, fish also plays an important role in the make-up of the FCS for non-fishers. When fish becomes rarer and hence more expensive, a reduction in animal protein intake of non-fishers could be the result–despite a redistribution of food expenditures. This is because other sources of animal protein may be more costly than fish is today.

---

[5] Animal protein scores in the FCS are calculated as the number of days animal protein is eaten weighted by 4.

[6] The scores for fruit and vegetables are weighted by 2.

[7] The high sugar consumption-adjusted upper threshold of borderline food consumption is set at 38.5.

Additionally, there are significant differences in some components of last week's FCS between fishers and non-fishers. Fishers have a more diverse diet, eating vegetables and animal proteins more often, while oil, milk, and sugar are consumed less often. Further decomposing the components of animal proteins in the FCS, it becomes apparent that fishers eat fish more often while scores for meat and eggs do not significantly differ between fishers and non-fishers. These results lead to the impression that fishers have a healthier, more nutritious diet than non-fishers because food from animal sources contains proteins and important micronutrients (Kawarazuka and Béné 2010). This is especially important in developing countries with their otherwise mostly staple-based diets. Red meat is often expensive and inaccessible by less affluent households. In contrast, fish is most important because it is easily available and small fish from capture fisheries are often eaten as a whole. This means it provides important micronutrients and has a higher nutritional quality than larger intensively farmed freshwater fish (Belton and Thilsted 2014).

Table 1: Two-sided *t*-tests for differences in different components of the FCS in fishing and non-fishing households in Stung Treng, Cambodia, pooled sample 2013 and 2014

Variable name		Whole sample	Non-fishing households	Fishing households	
Number of observations (n)		1163	403	760	
Total FCS		53.14	51.17	54.19	***
FCS by food groups	FCS staples	14	14	14	
	FCS pulses	3.65	3.66	3.65	
	FCS vegetables	4.26	4.06	4.37	***
	FCS fruit	3.01	2.87	3.08	
	FCS animal	22.65	20.59	23.74	***
	FCS milk	0.79	1.05	0.65	*
	FCS oil	1.81	1.89	1.77	**
	FCS sugar	2.98	3.04	2.94	*
FCS from animal	FCS fish	17.14	16.17	17.66	**
	FCS meat	3.35	2.88	3.61	
	FCS eggs	2.15	1.54	2.48	**

Significance levels: *p <0.01, **p <0.05, ***p <0.1.

Figure 3 shows how different food security indicators in the 25% income percentile compare between fishers and non-fishers. It tests for statistical differences in one-sided mean comparison tests. For the CSI, rCSI, and HFIAS lower scores indicate higher food security. In the FCS a higher score means higher food security. The rCSI and HFIAS show significantly less severe food insecurity in the worst month of the past year for fishing households. The FCSs for the different seasons in Figure 3 show a fluctuation of food security across the year. It is highest directly after harvest and lowest during the planting time which takes place in June and July, ~1–2 months after we collected the data. All indicators show that fishers face less seasonal food insecurity than non-fishers, albeit the differences are statistically insignificant for the CSI and the FCS in the post rice harvest season.

Figure 4 compares the differences in calorie and protein intakes between fishers and non-fishers in the whole sample and in the 25% income percentile. The distribution of fishing households across the lowest 25% income percentile is roughly similar to that of non-fishing households (Figure B1 in Appendix B). This makes the group of fishers and non-fishers in the lowest income percentile comparable. Figure 4 shows that the differences in calorie and protein intake between fishers and non-fishers are even

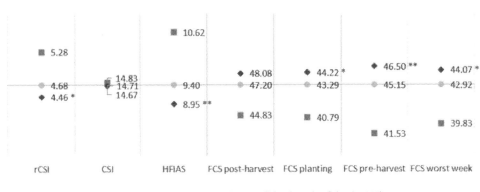

Figure 3: Comparison of Food Security Indicators in the 25% income percentile between fishers and non-fishers in Stung Treng, Cambodia. Two-sided *t* tests for different variable means between fishers and non-fishers. Sample from 2014 only as not all indicators are available from both survey waves. Significance Levels: *$p<0.1$, **$p<0.05$, ***$p<0.01$. Depicted data points are standardized around their mean; rCSI, CSI and HFIAS refer to the worst month in the past year

more pronounced in the 25% income percentile than in the whole sample. These differences largely stem from the fact that non-fishers in the 25% income percentile have considerably lower calorie and protein intakes than in the whole sample. For fishers the difference between the whole sample and the 25% percentile is not as pronounced. Almost all of the difference in protein intake between fishers and non-fishers in the 25% income percentile may be explained by the difference in proteins coming from fish. Meanwhile, only ~35% of the difference in the calorie consumption between fishers and non-fishers in the

25% percentile can be explained by differences in fish consumption. This confirms the opinion of Kawarazuka and Béné (2010; 2011) that fish is of special importance in poorer households.

To sum up, the findings in this section indicate that fishing households are more engaged in subsistence activities than non-fishing households and have lower cash income. We further show that fishers in the overall sample had a more nutritious diet in terms of proteins and calories in the past week. This finding is confirmed by higher FCSs and the FCS components of fishers for the last week. For the 25% income percentile

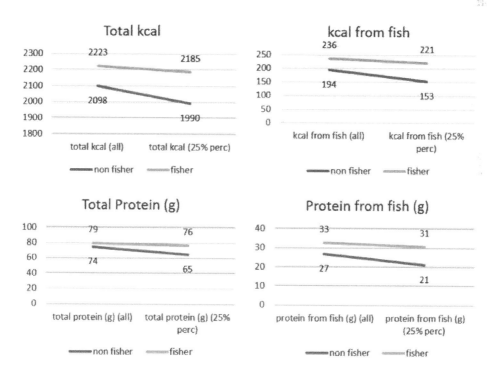

Figure 4: Comparison of nutrition variables of fishers and non-fishers in the whole sample and the 25% income percentile in StungTreng, Cambodia. All figures are per capita in adult equivalents. Pooled sample 2013 and 2014

we demonstrate that fishers faced less seasonal food insecurity in the past year. Furthermore, we show that fishing plays an even bigger role in the difference of nutrition between fishers and non-fishers in this income percentile than in the whole sample. Against these findings, we conclude that without subsequent adjustments of former fishers, a loss of fish stocks will lead to a permanent reduction in the food security of fishing households that is greater than the reduction felt by non-fishers. However, as fish is also an important component in the diet of non-fishing households, they will be affected by a reduced, more expensive supply of fish as well. Particularly poorer households who fish will feel the negative effects of fish stock decline as they may face more food insecurity across the year because their diets are most dependent on fish.

Conclusion

Considering the importance of small-scale fishing for rural livelihood outcomes in Cambodia and the expected decline of fish stocks in the Mekong River we asked how much fishing actually influences the diets of fishers in comparison to non-fishers, whether fish is of greater importance in the food security of poorer households than in others, and what the other typical income-earning strategies of fishing households are. The results from our descriptive analysis show that fishers enjoy a more nutritious diet than non-fishers. A large part of their protein intake is related to fish consumption. Nevertheless, fish is also an essential component in the diets of non-fishers.

For poorer households fishing is especially important as it is associated with reduced seasonal food insecurity and a lower gap in proteins and calories consumed in comparison to the whole population. Another important aspect is that fishing households rely more on subsistence activities and have less cash income than non-fishing households.

In the light of these findings the fact that fish stocks in the Mekong river system are expected to decline is alarming. This article clearly shows the importance of fish for the overall food security of fishing households in the area. Less fish and less catch will lead to decreasing levels of protein, calorie and micronutrient intake. Because fishing households have less cash income and rely more on subsistence activities, there will be a need to adjust agricultural production or increase activities earning cash income to replace the nutrients foregone from fishing. Furthermore, the poorer the household the more important fishing is to prevent seasonal food insecurity and the greater the role which fishing plays in nutrition. We conclude that households which go fishing are especially vulnerable to changes in the ecosystem of the river and need to develop alternative sources of income as fish stocks decline.

One of these alternative sources may be aquaculture. However, aquaculture is not an easy remedy. The poor, who benefit disproportionally from small-scale fishing, have more difficulties in investing into aquaculture. Furthermore, the large species produced may not replace the diverse micronutrients provided by small fish because they are not eaten as a whole, including the bones

(Welcomme et al. 2010). Moreover, the impact of this new technology on the river's ecosystem needs to be carefully explored before encouraging investment. Policies related to aquaculture should critically assess the role of aquaculture in the context of rural livelihood strategies and poverty alleviation (Bush 2004). Another alternative source of income may be increased agricultural production. Evidence from Thailand (Jutagate et al. 2003), Vietnam (Bui and Schreinemachers 2011), India (Duflo and Pande 2005), and China and Lesotho (Tilt, Braun, and He 2009) shows that a loss in natural capital due to dams can be partly compensated by more intense land use or an increase in household expenditures. However, these findings are influenced by compensation payments that play an important role to counteract the decrease in per capita income. The finding that an opening of the sluicegates of the Pak Mun Dam in Thailand led to an increase of traditional fishing activities and income from fishing (Jutagate et al. 2003) hints at the fact that the local population remains to prefer its original source of income over the adaptation situation.

While promoting economic development and advancing access to electricity in rural areas by building hydroelectric power stations, policymakers need to take into account the widespread dependence of households on fish in the area. These livelihoods have often been marginalized and neglected by policies favoring economic development in the Lower Mekong River basin in the past (Sneddon and Fox 2012). Trading-off food security for economic development, leaving those deprived of their living

to hope for trickle-down effects from economic development in the future does not suffice (Friend and Blake 2009; Arthur and Friend 2011). Before implementing new policies aiming at transforming the rural economy for future development, their impact on fishing-based livings should be carefully assessed and impact mitigation strategies for the most vulnerable households should be discussed. Ideally, economic development policy should be inclusive of those who are going to be negatively affected by its damage.

Further research needs to explore the role of substitution of fish with regard to both income and food security. Specifically, it would be interesting to know how households adjust their livelihood activities when income from fish declines, how much of fish protein can be substituted for by eating eggs and meat, and which households can successfully adapt to the new situation while others have difficulties in doing so. An interesting study area for this could be Thailand where important rivers have been dammed already in the 1990s. To overcome a shortcoming of our article, the fact that food security is only directly observed for one point in the year while measures of seasonal food insecurity have to be assessed retrospectively, seasonal food security and its relation to actual fish output in this season should be observed by repeating data collection in different times of the year. In addition, to gain insights into a broader level, data should be representative for the whole county or even the Mekong region.

Acknowledgment

The authors thankfully acknowledge the constructive comments by three anonymous reviewers of the World Food Policy Journal, the fruitful discussions with participants of the 2015 World Food Policy Conference and the help by their colleagues and the field staff who were involved in the data collection and cleaning process.

References

Ahmed, Mahfuzuddin, Hap Navy, Ly Vuthy, and Rav Santos. 1999."Fish Consumption Pattern in Major Freshwater Fisheries Provinces of Cambodia." *Naga, the ICLARM Quarterly* 22 (2): 27–31.

Ahmed, Mahfuzuddin, Hap Navy, Ly Vuthy, Marites Tiongco, Mekong River Commission, and others. 1998. *Socioeconomic Assessment of Freshwater CaptureFfisheries in Cambodia: Report on a Household Survey.* Phnom Penh, Cambodia: Mekong River Commission Phnom Penh.

Arthur, Robert I., and Richard Friend. 2011. "Inland Capture Fisheries in the Mekong and their Place and Potential within Food-Led Regional Development." *Global Environmental Change* 21 (1): 219–226.

Baran, Eric. 2005. *Cambodian Inland Fisheries: Facts, Figures and Context.* Vol. 1751. Phnom Penh, Cambodia: WorldFish.

Baran, Eric, Teemu Jantunen, and Chiew Kieok Chong. 2007. *Values of Inland Fisheries in the Mekong River Basin.* Phnom Penh, Cambodia: WorldFish.

Baran, Eric, and Chris Myschowoda. 2008. "Have Fish Catches been Declining in the Mekong River Basin." In *Modern Myths of the Mekong: A Critical Review of Water and Development Concepts, Principles and Policies*, eds. M. Kummu, M. Keskinen, and O. Varis. Helsinki: Helsinki University of Technology, 55–64.

Baran, Eric, and Chris Myschowoda. 2009. "Dams and Fisheries in the Mekong Basin." *Aquatic Ecosystem Health & Management* 12 (3): 227–234.

Belton, Ben, and Shakuntala H. Thilsted. 2014. "Fisheries in Transition: Food and Nutrition Security Implications for the Global South." *Global Food Security* 3 (1): 59–66.

Bezerra da Costa, Mikaelle K., Clarissy Dinyz de Melo, and Pricilla F. Macedo Lopes. 2014. "Fisheries Productivity and its Effects on the Consumption of Animal Protein and Food Sharing of Fishers' and Non-Fishers' Families." *Ecology of Food and Nutrition* 53 (4): 453–470.

Bühler, Dorothee, Ulrike Grote, Rebecca Hartje, Bopha Ker, Do Truong Lam, Loc Duc Nguyen, Trung Thanh Nguyen, and Kimsun Tong. 2015. "Rural Livelihood Strategies in Cambodia: Evidence from a Household Survey in Stung Treng." ZEF Working Paper, 137.

Bui, Thi M.H., and Pepijn Schrei-nemachers. 2011. "Resettling Farm Households in Northwestern Vietnam: Livelihood Change and Adaptation."

Water Resources Development 27 (4): 769–785.

Bush, Simon R. 2004. "A Political Ecology of Living Aquatic Resources in Lao PDR." PhD Dissertation. University of Sydney.

Christiaensen, Luc J., and Richard N. Boisvert. 2000. "On Measuring Household Food Vulnerability: Case Evidence from Northern Mali." Working Paper 2000-05.

Christiaensen, Luc J., Richard N. Boisvert, and John Hoddinott. 2000b. *Validating Operational Food Insecurity Indicators against a Dynamic Benchmark. Evidence from Mali*. Washington, DC: World Bank. Africa Region, Poverty Reduction and Social Development Unit.

Coates, Jennifer, Anne Swindale, and Paula Bilinsky. 2007. "Household Food Insecurity Access Scale (HFIAS) for Measurement of Food Access: Indicator Guide." Technical Report Series. USAID.

De Haen, Hartwig, Stephan Klasen, and Matin Qaim. 2011. "What do we Really Know? Metrics for Food Insecurity and Undernutrition." *Food Policy* 36 (6): 760–769.

Degen, Peter, and Nao Thuok. 1998. "Inland Fishery Management in Cambodia: Is the Fishing Lot System the Basis for Improved Management or should it be Abolished." Paper presented at the *Conference, Crossing Boundaries, the Seventh Biennial Conference of the International Association for the Study of Common Property*. Vancouver, British Columbia, Canada, June 10-14.

Deitchler, Megan, Terriand Ballard, Anne Swindale, and Jennifer Coates. 2011. "Introducing a Simple Measure of Household Hunger for Cross-Cultural Use." Technical Report Series, No. 12. USAID.

Dey, Madan M., Mohammed A. Rab, Ferdinand J. Paraguas, Somying Piumsombun, Ramachandra Bhatta, Md Ferdous Alam, and Mahfuzuddin Ahmed. 2005. "Fish Consumption and Food Security: A Disaggregated Analysis by Types of Fish and Classes of Consumers in Selected Asian countries." *Aquaculture Economics & Management* 9 (1): 89–111.

Duflo, Esther, and Rohini Pande. 2005. "Dams." NBER Working Paper Series, No. 11711.

Food and Agricultural Organization (FAO). 1996. "Rome Declaration on World Food Security and World Food Summit Plan of Action." In World Food Summit. Rome: *World Food Summit*, November 13-17.

Food and Agricultural Organization (FAO). 2003. *Myanmar Aquaculture and Inland Fisheries*. Bangkok: Food and Agricultural Organization.

Food and Agricultural Organization (FAO). 2013. "Smiling. Food Compostion Table for Cambodia." http://www.fao.org/infoods/infoods/tables-and-databases/asia/en/ [accessed September 30, 2015].

Food and Agricultural Organization (FAO). 2014. "ASEAN Food Composition Database Electronic Verison 1". Institute of Nutrition, Mahidol University, Thailand.

Friend, Richard M., and David JH Blake. 2009. "Negotiating Trade-offs in Water Resources Development in the Mekong Basin: Implications for Fisheries and Fishery-based Livelihoods." *Water Policy* 11 (1): 13–30.

Garaway, Caroline. 2005. "Fish, Fishing and the Rural Poor. A Case Study of the Household Importance of Small-Scale Fisheries in the Lao PDR." *Aquatic Resources, Culture and Development* 1 (2): 131–144.

Gomna, Ahmed, and Krishen Rana. 2007. "Inter-Household and Intra-Household Patterns of Fish and Meat Consumption in Fishing Communities in Two States in Nigeria." *British Journal of Nutrition* 97 (01): 145–152.

Hardeweg, Bernd, Stephan Klasen, and Hermann Waibel. 2013."Vulnerability to Poverty: Theory, Measurement and Determinants with Case Studies from Thailand and Vietnam." In *Vulnerability to Poverty: Theory, Measurement and Determinants*, eds. S. Klasen, and H. Waibel. Hampshire, UK: Palgrave Macmillan, 50–79.

Hatløy, Anne, Liv E. Torheim, and Arne Oshaug. 1998. "Food Variety—a Good Indicator of Nutritional Adequacy of the Diet? A Case Study from an Urban Area in Mali, West Africa." *European Journal of Clinical Nutrition* 52: 891–898.

Headey, Derek, and Oliver Ecker. 2013. "Rethinking the Measurement of Food Security: From First Principles to Best Practice." *Food Security* 5 (3): 327–343.

Hori, Mina, Satoshi Ishikawa, Ponley Heng, Somony Thay, Vuthy Ly, Thuok Nao, and Hisashi Kurokura. 2006. "Role of Small-Scale Fishing in Kompong Thom Province, Cambodia." *Fisheries Science* 72 (4): 846–854.

Hortle, Kent G. 2007. "Consumption and the Yield of Fish and other Aquatic Animals from the Lower Mekong Basin." MRC Technical Paper 16. 1–88.

Hortle, Kent G., S. Lieng, and John Valbo-Jorgensen. 2004. *An Introduction to Cambodia's Inland Fisheries (No. 4)*. Phnom Penh, Cambodia: Mekong River Commission.

Israel, Danilo C., Mahfuzuddin Ahmed, Elizabeth Petersen, Yeo B. Hong, and Hong M. Chee. 2007. "Economic Valuation of Aquatic Resources in Siem Reap Province, Cambodia." *Journal of Sustainable Agriculture* 31 (1): 111–135.

Jutagate, Tuantong, Chaiwut Krudpan, Praneet Ngamsnae, Kanjana Payooha, and Thanatip Lamkom. 2003. "Fisheries in the Mun River: A One-Year Trial of Opening the Sluice Gates of the Pak Mun Dam, Thailand." *Natural Science* 1 (37): 101–116.

Kawarazuka, Nozomi, and Christophe Béné. 2010. "Linking Small-Scale Fisheries and Aquaculture to Household Nutritional Security: An Overview." *Food Security* 2 (4): 343–357.

Kawarazuka, Nozomi, and Christophe Béné. 2011. "The Potential Role of Small Fish Species in Improving Micronutrient Deficiencies in Developing Countries:

Building Evidence." *Public Health Nutrition* 14 (11): 1927–1938.

Lam, Vwy, Wwl Cheung, W. Swarz, and Ur Sumaila. 2012. "Climate Change Impacts on Fisheries in West Africa: Implications for Economic, Food and Nutritional Security." *African Journal of Marine Science* 34 (1): 103–117.

Lovon, Margarita, and Astrid Mathiassen. 2014. "Are the World Food Programme's Food Consumption Groups a Good Proxy for Energy Deficiency?" *Food Security* 6 (4): 461–470.

Marschke, Melissa J., and Fikret Berkes. 2006. "Exploring Strategies that Build Livelihood Resilience: A Case from Cambodia." *Ecology and Society* 11 (1): 42.

Matsuishi, Takashi, Levi Muhoozi, Oliva Mkumbo, Yohana Budeba, Murithi Njiru, Ayub Asila, Andrew Othina, and Ian G. Cowx. 2006. "Are the Exploitation Pressures on the Nile Perch Fisheries Resources of Lake Victoria a Cause for Concern?" *Fisheries Management and Ecology* 13 (1): 53–71.

Maxwell, Daniel, Clement Ahiadeke, Carol Levin, Margaret Armar-Klemesu, Sawudatu Zakariah, and Grade M. Lampety. 1999. "Alternative Food-Security Indicators: Revisiting the Frequency and Severity of 'Coping Strategies." *Food Policy* 24: 411–429.

Maxwell, Daniel, and Richard Caldwell. 2008. "The Coping Strategies Index. Field Methods Manual." Technical Report, Vol. 2. USAID.

Maxwell, Daniel, Richard Caldwell, and Mark Langworthy. 2008. "Measuring Food Insecurity: Can an Indicator Based on Localized Coping Behaviors be Used to Compare Across Contexts?" *Food Policy* 33(6): 533–540.

Maxwell, Daniel, Bapu Vaitla, and Jennifer Coates. 2014. "How do Indicators of Household Food Insecurity Measure up? An Empirical Comparison from Ethiopia." *Food Policy* 47: 107–116.

Melgar-Quinonez, Hugo R., Ana C. Zubieta, Barbara MkNelly, Anastase Nteziyaremye, Maria F.D. Gerardo, and Christopher Dunford. 2006. "Household Food Insecurity and Food Expenditure in Bolivia, Burkina Faso, and the Philippines." *Journal of Nutrition* 136: 1431–1437.

NCDD. 2009. *Stung Treng Databook 2009*. Phnom Penh, Cambodia: National Committee for Sub-National Democratic Development.

Navy, Hap, and Madhusudan Bhattarai. 2009. "Economics and Livelihoods of Small-Scale Inland Fisheries in the Lower Mekong Basin: A Survey of Three Communities in Cambodia." *Water Policy* 11 (Supplement 1): 31–51.

Nguyen, Trung T., Truong L. Do, Dorothee Bühler, Rebecca Hartje, and Ulrike Grote. 2015. "Rural Livelihoods and Environmental Resource Dependence in Cambodia." *Ecological Economics* 120: 282–295.

Orr, Stuart, Jamie Pittock, Ashok Chapagain, and David Dumaresq. 2012.

"Dams on the Mekong River: Lost Fish Protein and the Implications for Land and Water Resources." *Global Environmental Change* 22 (4): 925–932. doi: http://dx.doi.org/10.1016/j.gloenvcha.2012.06.002.

Pukinskis, Ilse, and Kim Geheb. 2012. "The Impacts of Dams on the Fisheries of Mekong." *State of Knowledge Series, 1.*

Pukinskis, I. and Geheb, K. 2012. *The Impact of Dams on the Fisheries of the Mekong.* State of Knowledge Series 1. Vientiane, Lao PDR, Challenge Program on Water and Food.

Roberts, Tyson R., and Ian G. Baird. 1995. "Traditional Fisheries and Fish Ecology on the Mekong River at Khone Waterfalls in Southern Laos." *Natural History Bulletin of the Siam Society* 43 (2): 219–262.

Ruel, Marie T. 2002. "Is Dietary Diversity an Indicator of Food Security or Dietary Quality? A Review of Measurement Issues and Research Needs." Discussion Paper, No. 140. IFPRI.

Smith, Laurence E., Sophie Nguyen Khoa, and Kai Lorenzen. 2005. "Livelihood Functions of Inland Fisheries: Policy Implications in Developing Countries." *Water Policy* 7 (4): 359–383.

Sneddon, Christopher, and Coleen Fox. 2012. "Inland Capture Fisheries and Large River Systems: A Political Economy of Mekong Fisheries." *Journal of Agrarian Change* 12 (2-3): 279–299.

Steyn, Nelia P., Johanna H. Nel, Guy Nantel, Gina Kennedy, and Demetre Labadarios. 2006. "Food Variety and Dietary Diversity Scores in Children: Are they Good Indicators of Dietary Adequacy?" *Public Health Nutrition* 9 (05): 644–650.

Sultana, Parvin, and Paul M. Thompson. 2007. "Community Based Fisheries Management and Fisher Livelihoods: Bangladesh Case Studies." *Human Ecology* 35 (5): 527–546.

Svedberg, Peter. 2002. "Undernutrition Overestimated." *Economic Development and Cultural Change* 51 (1): 5–36.

Tilt, Bryan, Yvonne Braun, and Daming He. 2009. "Social Impacts of Large Dams Projects: A Comparison of International Case Studies and Implications for Best Practice." *Journal of Environmental Management* 90: S249–S257.

United Nations (UN). 2008. *Designing Household Survey Samples: Practical Guidelines.* New York: United Nations Publications.

Van Zalinge, Nicolaas, S.T. Nao, S.T. Touch, and L. Deap. 2000. "Common Property in the Mekong: Issues of Sustainability and Subsistence." In *ICLARM (International Center for Living Aquatic Resources Management) Studies and Reviews,* eds. M. Ahmend, and P. Hirsch, 37–48.

Welcomme, Robin L., Ian G. Cowx, David Coates, Christophe Béné, Simon Funge-Smith, Ashley Halls, and Kai Lorenzen. 2010. "Inland Capture Fisheries." *Philosophical Transactions of the Royal Society B: Biological Sciences* 365 (1554): 2881–2896.

Wiesmann, Doris, Lucy Bassett, Todd Benson, and John Hoddinott. 2009. "Validation of the World Food Programme s Food Consumption Score and Alternative Indicators of Household Food Security." Discussion Paper 00870. IFPRI.

World Food Programme (WFP). 2008. *Food Consumption Analysis. Calculation and Use of the Food Consumption Score in Food Security Analysis*. Rome, Italy: United Nations World Food Programme.

World Health Organization (WHO). 1985. *Energy and Protein Requirements, No. 724*. Geneva: World Health Organization.

Ziv, Guy, Eric Baran, So Nam, Ignacio Rodriguez-Iturbe, and Simon A. Levin. 2012. "Trading-off Fish Biodiversity, Food Security, and Hydropower in the Mekong River Basin." *Proceedings of the National Academy of Sciences* 109 (15): 5609–5614.

Appendix A

Construction of the Food Security Indicators used

The Food Consumption Score

The construction of the food consumption score (FCS) is based on the technical report on the FCS issued by the World Food Programme (2008). For its construction food groups are formed and days of consumption per food group are counted at household level. The food groups are (weights within parentheses): main staples (2), pulses (3), vegetables (1), fruit (1), meat, fish and eggs (4), milk (4), sugar (0.5), oil (0.5), and condiments (0). According to their nutritious value the quantities per food group are weighted to calculate the FCS of household *i* as follows:

$$FCS_i = \sum_{g=1}^{9} f_g * w_g \qquad (1)$$

Where f_g represents food group g and w_g is its respective weight. We use the FCS as a constant score in our analysis instead of grouping households into food security groups according to the FCS. The reason for this is that we want to focus on the general improvement of the absolute nutrition situation in a household due to fishing which is captured by the total FCS rather than wanting to judge who is food secure and who is not according to a predefined cut-off point.

The Household Food Insecurity Access Scale

The household food insecurity access scale HFIAS is computed following the methodology laid out by USAID (Coates, Swindale, and Bilinsky 2007). The indicator measures household food insecurity access as a continuous score. Normally it has a recall period of 1 month. It is based on a set of nine questions which first ask about the occurrence of food insecurity events (Did your family not have enough to eat?) and in a second step about the frequency of their occurrence (How often did you family not have enough to eat?). Adjusting the index to account for site specific characteristics, we used nine questions and asked respondents to answer the questions for the worst week in the past year (see Table A1 for list of questions and exact wording

used in the survey). The adjustment of the recall period was necessary to keep the questionnaire as short as possible and to avoid asking similar questions twice. Furthermore, instead of asking separately for occurrence and frequency we combined both things in one question.

To construct the frequency-of-occurrence we multiply the number of days reported for each question in the worst week by four to proxy for the worst month and code these frequencies into three categories: 1—rarely (0–2 days per month), 2— sometimes (3–10 times per month), and 3—often (>10 times per month).The result is a frequency of occurrence score for each question in each household in the range of 0–3. These frequencies of occurrence scores are then added up across all questions for each household, resulting in the HFIAS for the household.

Table A1 HFIAS questions asked in the questionnaire

No.	For the worst week between 05/13 and 04/14 please indicate the number of days that your household experienced the following:
1	… you worried that the household would not have enough food?
2	… you were not able to eat the kinds of food you preferred?
3	… you ate a limited variety of foods?
4	… you ate some foods you really did not want to eat?
5	… you ate a smaller meal than you felt you needed?
6	… you ate fewer meals in a day?
7	… there was not food of any kind in the household?
8	… you went a whole day and night without eating?
9	… you went to sleep at night hungry?

The Coping Strategies Index (CSI) and reduced Coping Strategies Index

The coping strategies index (CSI) and reduced coping strategies index (rCSI) measure household coping behavior which is related to household food insecurity events (Maxwell and Caldwell 2008). Coping strategies are usually easier to observe and it is less costly and time intensive to collect data compared to household food consumption levels. The CSI is created in four steps based on the Field Manual from USAID (Maxwell and Caldwell 2008): First, the locally relevant coping strategies are identified through four Focus Group Discussions (FGD) in the field from a list of possible generally possible strategies. Second, the data collection process counts how often strategies were applied by a household using a recall period of 1 week. Specifically we asked households to report the number of days they used the coping strategies in the worst week of the past year. The questions asked to the households in Stung Treng are displayed in Table A2. Third, based on the FGD, the different coping strategies are categorized according to their severity and the categories are used to weight the strategies. The weights used in this calculation are based on four FGDs in villages that were part of the survey sample and are depicted in Table A3. Finally, the frequency answers for each question are multiplied by the according weight and the resulting scores are added up for each household to generate the CSI.

Table A2 CSI questions as asked in the questionnaire

No.	For the worst week between 05/13 and 04/14 please indicate the number of days that your household experienced the following:
1	… you were not able to eat the kinds of food you preferred?
2	… you borrowed food or relied on help from a friend or relative?
3	… you purchased food on credit?
4	… you gathered wild food or hunted?
5	… you harvested immature crops?
6	… you consumed see stock held for next season?
7	… you sent household members to elsewhere?
8	… you sent household members to beg?
9	… you ate a smaller mean than you felt you needed?
10	… you fed working members at the expense of non-working members?
11	… you ate fewer meals in a day?
12	… you restricted consumption by adults in order for small children to eat?
13	… you went a whole day and night without eating?

Table A3 Weights applied per question

No.	For the worst week between 05/13 and 04/14 please indicate the number of days that your household experienced the following:	Weight
1	… you were not able to eat the kinds of food you preferred?	2.75
2	… you borrowed food or relied on help from a friend or relative?	1
3	… you purchased food on credit?	2.25
4	… you gathered wild food or hunted?	2.25
5	… you harvested immature crops?	3.5
6	… you consumed see stock held for next season?	4
7	… you sent household members to elsewhere?	3.5
8	… you sent household members to beg?	3.5
9	… you ate a smaller mean than you felt you needed?	2
10	… you fed working members at the expense of non-working members?	2.5
11	… you ate fewer meals in a day?	2.5
12	… you restricted consumption by adults in order for small children to eat?	2.25
13	… you went a whole day and night without eating?	3.5

As the CSI is site specific, the reduced or comparative CSI was developed to enable comparison across contexts (Maxwell, Caldwell, and Langworthy 2008). The rCSi is based on a subset of only five questions (see Table A4) and has universal weights. These questions are based on coping behaviors found to be applied across many countries. The rCSI reflects food security nearly as good as the CSI (Maxwell, Caldwell, and Langworthy 2008).

Table A4 rCSI questions as asked in the questionnaire and universal weights

No.	For the worst week between 05/13 and 04/14 please indicate the number of days that your household experienced the following:	Universal Weight
1	… you were not able to eat the kinds of food you preferred?	1
2	… you borrowed food or relied on help from a friend or relative?	2
3	… you ate a smaller mean than you felt you needed?	1
4	… you ate fewer meals in a day?	3
5	… you restricted consumption by adults in order for small children to eat?	1

Calorie and Protein Intakes per Adult Equivalent

To calculate per capita calorie and protein intakes we use the food items and quantities consumed as reported by the household for the past 7 days which are converted using food composition tables by the FAO (2013; 2014). These values are then divided by the number of adult equivalent household members respectively. The conversion of household members to adult equivalent members is based on WHO (1985).

Appendix B

Supplementary statistics of the characteristics of fishing households

Table B1: Comparison of characteristics in the whole sample, fishing and non-fishing households; Two-sided *t*-tests for different variable means between fishers and non-fishers, pooled sample 2013 and 2014; Significance Levels: * *p*<0.1, ** *p*<0.05, *** *p*<0.01

Variable name	Whole sample	non-fishing	fishing
Number of observations (n)	1163	403	760
Household size	5.22	4.83	5.43 ***
Female household head (dummy)	0.12	0.16	0.1 ***
Khmer (dummy)	0.82	0.85	0.8 **
Tropical Livestock Units (TLU) consumed per capita	0.01	0.01	0.01
TLU sold per capita	0.1	0.1	0.11
Value of productive assets in 2005 PPP$	2665.27	2790.44	2598.9
Annual income per capita in 2005 PPP$	1061.77	1200.54	988.19 ***
Additional food expenditure per capita in 2005 PPP$	175.38	265.49	127.6 ***

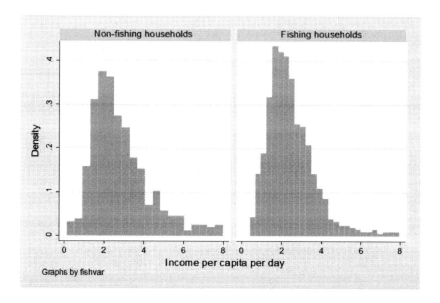

Figure B1: Income distribution of fishers and non-fishers in Stung Treng, Cambodia, in the pooled sample 2013 and 2014

Developing Local Sustainable Seafood Markets: A Thai Example

Courtney Kehoe[A], Melissa Marschke[A], Wichitta Uttamamunee[B], Jawanit Kittitornkool[B] & Peter Vandergeest[C]

Increasing awareness of degradation in ocean ecologies and fisheries has made seafood a leading edge in the green marketing movement, with most major buyers in the global North committing to buying seafood that has been certified as sustainable. But what about the significant and growing Asian markets, where seafood has become a healthy and prestigious food choice among wealthier consumers? Is it possible to develop a market for sustainably produced seafood among Asian consumers motivated by civil and ecological concerns? To address these questions our research traces how a Thai Fisherfolk Shop, located 4 hours to the south of Bangkok, has worked to develop an alternative market for seafood caught by local, small-scale fishers. Although we find that there is a mismatch between the volume of aquatic species that fishers catch, the ability of the Shop to process, store, and sell seafood, and consumer demand, our analysis suggests that it is possible to create a market for small-scale, sustainably sourced seafood in Thailand.

Keywords: *small-scale fishers, sustainable seafood, conventions theory, consumer awareness, Asian markets*

Introduction

The sustainable seafood movement began nearly two decades ago in response to failing fisheries management and the subsequent degradation of ocean ecologies and fisheries (Jacquet and Pauly 2007; Konefal 2013). Driven largely by nongovernmental organizations (NGO), industry, and the private sector, this movement sought to fill a governance gap through the use of market mechanisms like third-party certification and ecolabeling. Under ecolabeling schemes, retailers and food companies seek to enhance brand value through an association with sustainability. Producers, in turn, may gain access to particular markets for sustainably harvested seafood, often in the EU and in North America. Although the effectiveness of these mechanisms in terms of their ability to increase ecological sustainability remains unclear, ecolabeling continues to grow in prominence (Lay 2012; Ponte 2012; Hallstein and Villas-Boas 2013).

[A] University of Ottawa, Canada

[B] Prince of Songkla University, Thailand

[C] York University, Canada

doi: 10.18278/wfp.2.2.3.1.3

Within the seafood sector, a large number of competing management practices and standards have developed— some global, some national, and others targeting specific species or fishing methods—with over 30 fisheries ecolabels in existence (Jacquet et al. 2010; Roheim 2009; Parkes et al. 2010). The dominant global sustainability standard for wild catch fisheries is the Marine Stewardship Council (MSC) (Blackmore and Norbury 2015): ~12 percent of world fisheries production is currently MSC certified, although this market is generally limited to species consumed in the North (Belton and Bush 2014; Bush et al. 2013; Marine Stewardship Council 2014). MSC has single-handedly created "sustainable fish" as a commodity that has been brought into mainstream retail in North America and Europe (i.e., Walmart and Carrefour) (Ponte 2012; Vandergeest, Ponte, and Bush 2015). A significant portion of producers and consumers of lower level trophic species, however, are being excluded from such markets.

Asia, as a region, has substantial potential in terms of marketing local sustainable seafood: 84 percent of all people employed in fisheries and aquaculture live in Asia (over 58 million people) (Food and Agriculture Organization 2014). As a food source, fish continues to be a major source of animal protein and plays an especially important role in many vulnerable rural and coastal communities (Belton and Thilsted 2014). Fish also play a central role in culture and cuisine in inland and coastal regions, and the continuing rise of an urban middle class is likely to result in even higher levels of demand for seafood products. Consumer surveys in Thailand show a substantial market for organic foods and related labels, with consumers willing to pay high premiums (Posri, Shankar, and Chadbunchachai 2006; Roitner-Schobesberger et al. 2008; Sangkumchaliang and Huang 2012a). The question is whether this interest could be extended to sustainable seafood, as the motivation for organic consumers seems to be primarily about health and safety.

Our article explores the possibility of expanding coverage of sustainable seafood through tapping national markets and the degree to which such markets can respond to the interests of small-scale producers. The article traces how a Thai Fisherfolk Shop—referred to throughout this article as the Shop—located 4 hours south of Bangkok has worked to develop an alternative market for seafood caught by small-scale fishers. This Shop is one of a planned network of such shops throughout Thailand, marketing seafood caught mainly from the Gulf of Thailand. We begin our article by analyzing the type of aquatic species caught by local fishers that the Shop procures seafood from, before turning to an assessment of how the Shop more generally procures, processes, and sells sustainable seafood. We then consider why consumers are willing to pay premium prices for local, sustainably sourced seafood, drawing on conventions theory to aid in our analysis, and reflect upon the challenges facing fishers, the Shop, and consumers to ensure a fit between supply, demand, and sustainability. We argue that this case provides evidence of how a local sustainable seafood movement can meet multiple demands and support a move toward social-ecological sustainability in the fisheries.

Understanding sustainable food movements

Conventions theory has influenced various branches of agro-food studies, providing analytical guidance and theoretical insight for examining alternative food networks and the so-called "quality turn" in food production and consumption (Ponte 2016). Building on the formative work of Boltanski and Thévenot (1991), conventions theory introduced sociological considerations to reconcile economic conventions within wider frameworks of evaluation, highlighting the plurality of forms of justification that may exist for an action such as the choice of what type of seafood to purchase (Migliore, Schifani, and Cembalo 2015). In conventions theory, markets are defined or guided by a distinct set of principles and values under which goods become qualified for trade and to which trade is then subsequently managed (Ponte 2016).

Six ideal-type "orders of worth" are identified to illustrate how these principles and values are used to frame the justification of human interaction and economic practice (Ponte and Sturgeon 2014) (see Table 1). Each order of worth has a different justification. For instance, market conventions refer to an understanding that difference in price signifies difference in quality, whereas industrial conventions seek to legitimize quality vis-à-vis establishing third-party verification schemes like certification or other branding mechanisms. These differ from domestic quality conventions (determined through trust, history, locality, and personal ties) or civic quality conventions (linked to welfare and impact on society or the environment) (Ponte and Sturgeon 2014). Opinion quality is another "order of worth," whereby the views of experts or the newness of a product are taken into account (Ponte and Sturgeon 2014). The typology presented in conventions theory is not intended to be exhaustive, rather to enable an analysis of the justifications found in the majority of ordinary situations (Evans 2011).

Adopting an "order of worth" approach (Ponte 2016), we attribute one or a combination of conventions to understand the choices urban Thai consumers make in purchasing local, sustainable seafood. We anticipate that a sustainable seafood movement would incorporate a mix of these conventions, with the "sustainable" aspect implying some commitment to civic quality conventions among producers, processors, and intermediaries, and consumers, along with a commitment to the ecological welfare of the oceans. Meanwhile, because sustainability is associated with small-scale fishers in Thailand, there is likely a commitment to domestic quality conventions too— especially given the interest in supporting the livelihoods of local fishers and the small-scale nature of the Shop. We return to conventions theory later in the paper.

In Asia, sustainability in marine capture fisheries is an emerging area focused primarily on domestic markets. This is in contrast to aquaculture sustainability, which has been in place for export markets since 2000 (Vandergeest 2007). Within the Thai context, this shift in focus toward sustainability is captured in part by a "quality turn," whereby domestic consumer interest in health and

Table 1: The orders of worth

Convention	Organizing principle	Focus of justification
Market	Competitiveness	Product units
Civic	Representation	Negotiation, consultation, and distributional arrangements
Domestic	Loyalty	Specific assets
Opinion	Reputation	Public relations, media coverage, and brand reputation
Inspired	Creativity	Innovation and creation
Industrial	Productivity	Plans, systems, controls, and forecasts

Adapted from: Boltanski and Thevenot 1991; Ponte and Sturgeon 2014

safety of food is growing (Srithamma, Vithayarungruangsri, and Posayanonda 2005; Sangkumchaliang and Huang 2012b; Kelly et al. 2015). The interest tends to be embedded in practices of quality assurance, traceability, geographic origin, sustainable agro-ecological practices, and direct marketing schemes (Ponte 2016). As such, the Thai government, industry, and local NGO (e.g., the Thai Sea Watch Association) are attempting to establish one or more national ecolabeling schemes. Given these changing attitudes, and the challenges of social-ecological sustainability in Thailand's short and long haul sectors (Marschke and Vandergeest 2016), there is an interest in supporting local fishers. This case seeks to better understand the experiences of one Shop attempting to create a niche market for local, sustainable seafood.

Approach, study area, and methods

In June 2014, seven fisher groups, each representing fishers from a particular village in Prachuap Khiri Khan province, Thailand, came together with the help of the Thai Sea Watch Association (TSWA) NGO to set up the Shop. The purpose of the Shop was to: (a) initiate an alternative market by directly supplying consumers with seafood from small-scale fishers using nondestructive fishing gear; (b) provide consumers with quality seafood; and

(c) set up channels for disseminating information and educating the public about marine conservation. Within the seven small-scale fisher groups, 66 fishers contributed 50,000 THB (~1500 USD[1], or just over 22 USD each) to the start-up of the Shop. The Shop also received significant budget support from Oxfam and investment from the Federation of Thai Fisherfolk Association. When the Shop was envisioned, stakeholders thought that seafood could be sourced exclusively from those fishers who initially contributed to the development of the Shop based upon the seasonality of their product.

The methodological approach of our article is twofold: (a) case-specific research with fishers, Shop employees, and consumers and (b) an assessment of Shop procurement and sales practices to assess the economic viability of the Shop. Data collection included conducting interviews with consumers buying Shop seafood ($n=12$), key informant interviews with Shop staff ($n=3$) and with fishers ($n=31$), a focus group with fishers ($n=6$), and an analysis of Shop receipts detailing procurement of seafood and consumer sales from June 2014 to May 2015 (5371 receipts). Purchasing and sales data enabled us to gain a detailed understanding of the amount of seafood purchased, processed, and sold in Year 1 of Shop operations. Two of the authors also engaged in participant observation with fishers and Shop employees, complimented by time in Bangkok

helping to sell Shop fish in the Spring and Summer of 2015.

Key informant interview questions with fishers and Shop employees centered around five themes: background of involvement, knowledge of the Shop, operation of the Shop, supply chain management, and sustainability of the Shop. Consumer interviews, which focused on purchasing behavior, seafood consumption, and perceptions of the Shop, were carried out in two ways: (a) through random selection from the Shop's LINE account—a smart phone application that allows consumers to subscribe to the Shop's group, view product, and place orders—after which, participants were spoken with via video conference call ($n=5$) or telephone ($n=3$); and (b) face-to-face interviews ($n=4$) with consumers as they were purchasing Shop fish at a small urban farm in central Bangkok. A preliminary reflection of the characteristics of urban consumers who purchase Shop seafood suggests that consumers are largely female, single, with an undergraduate education, living with two or three people in the household.

Results

Seafood caught by local fishers

While seven small-scale fishing groups supply the majority of seafood to the Shop, key informant interviews focused on one

---

[1] Currency is converted from Thai Baht to United States Dollar using the average exchange rate (1 THB = 0.03 USD) for the duration of the study period (June 2014–October 2015).

fishing group in the village of Khan Kradai. Fishers here catch an array of species annually, often in the form of bycatc[2] since most fishers target one or more of six main species: short-bodied mackerel, Indo-Pacific king mackerel, goldstripe sardinella, blue swimming crab, splendid squid, and banana shrimp. Catch averages per trip and per species vary greatly (5–500 kg) (Table 2), with fishers using hook and lines, surface gill nets, bottom gill nets, and trammel nets with differing mesh sizes to target particular species (e.g., bottom gill nets of 4.5 cm mesh size are used to target short-bodied mackerel compared with surface gill nets with a mesh size of 2.9 cm that target goldstripe sardinella). These species are sold daily to the middleperson (MP) or to the Shop when the Shop is purchasing local seafood. Since the Shop pays considerably higher prices for local seafood than the MP (Table 2), fishers prefer to sell to the Shop when possible.

Table 2: Main species and price premiums in one village

Targeted fish species	Seasonality	Average kilograms per trip[a]	Price paid by MP[b] (Baht)	Price paid by Shop (Baht)	Price premium (Baht, %)
Banana shrimp, small			300	385	85 (28.3)
Banana shrimp, medium	Nov–Jan	5–10	400	484	84 (21.0)
Banana shrimp, large			500	578	78 (15.6)
Blue swimming crab	Oct–Jan	5–10	200	301	101 (50.5)
Goldstripe sardinella	Sept–Nov	300–500	8	22	14 (275.0)
Indo-Pacific king mackerel	Sep–Nov	10–30	190	209	19 (10.0)
Short-bodied mackerel	Jan–Mar, Sept–	100–300	40	45	5 (10.0)
Splendid squid	Sept–Nov	10–20	115	245	130 (113.0)

Source: Focus group discussion and interviews

[a] The amount of species caught fluctuates throughout the year, with fishers catching higher volumes during peak season (e.g., fishers can catch 1000 kg or more of short-bodied mackerel or goldstripe sardinella in a single trip)
[b] The price offered by a MP or the Shop also fluctuates according to supply and demand. The Shop prices above are calculated yearly averages, whereas the price paid by the MP is based on one focus group.

---

[2] The type and total bycatch varies depending on gear used. According to fishers, when using trammel nets up to 80 percent of catch per trip is comprised of non-target species such as tiger-toothed croaker, four finger threadfin, and soft cuttlefish, whereas bycatch from hook and line (e.g., Indo-Pacific sail-fish, barracuda, and emperor red snapper) amounts to only 1 percent of total catch per trip.

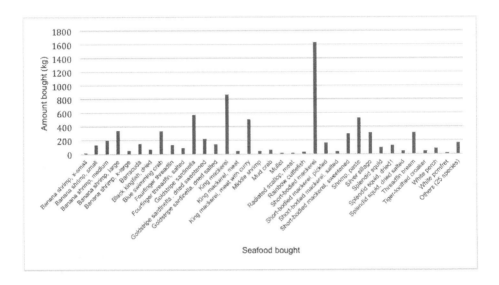

Figure 1: Seafood purchased by the Shop
Source: Shop buying receipts, 2014–2015

Seafood purchased by the Shop

The Shop's mandate is to buy local seafood, with 95.5 percent of the Shop's product being sourced within Prachuap Khiri Khan province where the Shop is located. During its first year of operation, the Shop procured a total of 7,972.38 kg of seafood: 7,610.67 kg from Prachuap Khiri Khan and the rest from southern Thailand (236.56 kg from Nakhon Si Thammarat, 99 kg from Trang, and 28.60 kg from Phattalung). Most species that the Shop sourced were local, from the seven fishing groups, including banana shrimp, goldstripe sardinella, short-bodied mackerel, threadfin bream, middle shrimp, and blue swimming crab. A few species such as Indo-Pacific king mackerel, white pomfret, barracuda, and

fourfinger threadfin were procured both locally and from southern provinces, while lined silver grunt, striped sea catfish, queen fish, and siamese glassfish were sourced exclusively from southern Thai provinces.

In Year 1, 59 distinct seafood products were bought (i.e., whole fish, shrimp of various sizes, some aquatic species that had already been dried, salted or sweetened). As Figure 1 shows, short-bodied mackerel was the most common species purchased (a total of 2,141 kg when factoring both raw and processed product), although the Shop sourced small amounts of multiple other species to also meet consumer demand. Species sourced from provinces in Southern Thailand are an example of this, as often only a few kilograms of a particular type were sourced[3]. Worth highlighting, over 92 percent of seafood sourced through the Shop was done directly with fishers rather than though a MP: this enables the Shop to build a relationship directly with fishers and ensures that fishers receive a price premium for their seafood. While the average price per kilogram of seafood procured was 228.88 THB (6.87 USD), some species proved to be costlier than others. White pomfret cost 716.67 THB (21.51 USD) per kilogram, whereas pickled short-bodied mackerel could be bought for as little as 40 THB (1.20 USD) per kilogram.

The Shop purchased seafood products that had already been processed by fishers, their families, or community members. In such instances, the Shop paid a higher price for these seafood products since they required less of the Shop's resources (labor in particular). For example, the Shop paid 65 THB (1.95 USD) for sweetened short-bodied mackerel compared to the 43.37 THB (1.29 USD) paid for unprocessed short-bodied mackerel. This seafood product was then resold for a handsome profit (400 THB or 12 USD). Such practices help the Shop to satisfy consumer interest in an array of seafood products, from buying an entire fish to buying fish that has already been prepared in a curry.

Seafood sold to consumers by the Shop

Most seafood is sold to retailers or consumers in Bangkok (5071 kg), with only small amounts of fish sold in the province of origin (Prachuap) (737 kg) or in southern Thailand (42 kg). Since Bangkok is only a 4-hour drive away, Shop staff can pack and transport fresh seafood in a timely manner, while also selling processed seafood that stores for longer periods of time (e.g., dried or salted fish, or fish paste). Two-thirds of Shop sales (3899 kg) take place in the store[4] or through selling at farmers' markets in Bangkok. An emerging trend, however, is online sales (1781 kg). Nearly one-third of sales are done via home delivery, whereby consumers order a particular kind of seafood and the Shop then sends this directly to a consumers' home in Bangkok. Since only one of the Shop employees drives a car, seafood sold this way is either shipped through the post office or transported by van to Bangkok where consumers can either pick it up at the Victory Monument transport hub or have it motorcycled directly to their home. While the amount of seafood product sold to third-party retailers in the first year of operations was miniscule (170 kg) in comparison, as demand from Lemon Farm (a chain of organic supermarkets in Bangkok) and other Thai retailers increases, this percentage will also increase.

---

[3] For example, only 3.10 kg of lined silver grunt, 1.20 kg of striped sea catfish, 6.50 kg of queenfish, and 5 kg siamese glassfish were bought.

[4] In store sales include orders placed by consumers via telephone or the Shop's Line application as well as purchases made physically at the FisherFolk Shop.

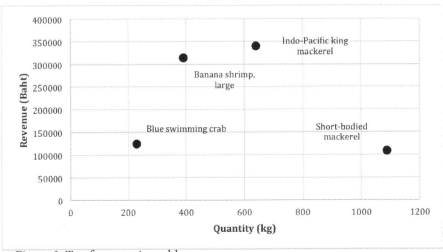

Figure 2: Top four species sold
Source: Shop buying receipts, 2014–2015

In Year 1, the Shop's top three revenue-generating species were Indo-Pacific king mackerel, large-sized banana shrimp, and blue swimming crab. These three species brought in a total of 340,169.65 THB (10,205.09 USD), 313,972.23 THB (9419.17 USD) and 124,613.55 THB (3738.41 USD), respectively. Yet, in terms of volume, short-bodied mackerel was the most popular species with 1086.67 kg sold (Figure 2). This does not even take into account the sale of processed short-bodied mackerel which is prepared in 1 of 11 ways: boiled sweetened, dried, dried-salted, salted, fried, sweetened, steamed, without the fish head, pickled, with noodles, or with chili powder. These aforementioned four species represent two thirds of the main species targeted by fishers in the area.

The Shop sells 79 distinct seafood products. Of the 42 processed seafood products sold by the Shop in 2015, 29 are processed in Shop, whereas the other 14 are processed by fishers, their families, or community members and then bought by the Shop. Drying, salting, sweetening, steaming, or creating a sauce for various species is something the Shop does as a way of broadening consumer choice. For example, in addition to short-bodied mackerel processed in 1 of 11 ways, dried or salted versions of banana shrimp, fourfinger threadfin, goldstripe sardinella, mullet, threadfin bream, tiger-toothed croaker, and yellowstripe scad are also popular, as are eggs (from blue swimming crab and white perch) and shrimp paste; over 300 kg of shrimp paste was sold in the first year of operations. Shop employees believe that processing can increase consumer interest in local seafood, through a variety of taste options, along with increasing the revenue earned by the Shop since processed seafood products are sold at a higher price.

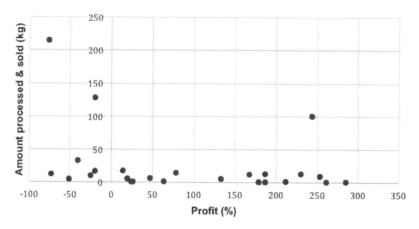

Figure 3: Profitability of products processed by the Shop[a]
[a] Further details can be found in the Supplementary Data
Source: Shop buying receipts, 2014–2015

Drawing on a year of purchasing and sales receipts, we calculated the profitability[5] of processing (relative to total cost) for 25 of the 29 seafood products processed by the Shop[6]. Our analysis suggests that the processing of seafood may not be where the Shop should place its efforts. In Figure 3, the concentration of data points near the origin of the graph and to the left of the Y-axis indicates relatively small or negative profits for certain types of processed seafood products. Note that if the Shop were processing seafood in a way that boosted revenue, we would expect to see far more data points to the right of the Y-axis (ideally in the upper right-hand corner): this would indicate that the more profitable species are being sold in larger quantities.

Instead Figure 3 shows that the Shop is selling seafood products that incur loss, often times in large amounts as is the case with short-bodied mackerel with noodle (of which 214.14 kg are sold at a net loss of ~75 percent). Other species that are not profitable include: dried-salted splendid squid, blue swimming crab meat, mantis shrimp meat, dried-salted mullet, and the king

[5] Profit calculations take into account the cost of raw materials (i.e., species), labor, and utilities such as electricity and water. The calculations do not consider the additional monies spent on sugar, salt and other ingredients necessary for processing.

[6] Value added was not calculated for four seafood products (blue swimming crab eggs, Indo-Pacific king mackerel eggs, white pomfret eggs, and Indo-Pacific king-mackerel body).

mackerel burger. The loss associated with processing these seven species on the left of the Y-axis (–86,902.51 THB or 2607.07 USD) outweighs the benefit derived from those 18 species on the right of the Y-axis (38,993 THB or 1,169.79 USD). Fried short-bodied mackerel is one example of the Shop generating significant revenue from seafood processing, with 100.30 kg being sold for a net profit of nearly 250 percent; more time, effort, and resources should be put into creating such items.

Consumer interest in Shop seafood products

Individuals purchasing from the Shop do so primarily for three reasons: (a) health and safety; (b) environmental benefits; and (c) support for small-scale fishers. We return to conventions theory as a way to analyze consumer choice in buying sustainable seafood (Ponte 2016). The categories of market, industrial, domestic, civic, and opinion quality[7] enable us to analyze socially constructed norms that lay behind consumer motives to purchase sustainable seafood (Campbell and MacRae 2013). Our initial analysis suggests that consumers support local sustainable seafood for multiple reasons.

Three quarters of interviewed consumers were willing to pay a premium on locally caught seafood, motivated by market quality conventions. Consumers measure market quality in terms of health and safety, particularly the absence of chemicals such as formalin in the production process. Aesthetics, described as a demand for "beautiful" fish, and freshness also play a role, especially for those consumers who equate freshness with greater nutritional value. One consumer claimed that product from the Shop is "more clean and fresh than at the normal market" (008[8]). However, domestic quality conventions also matters, as one consumer indicated that they buy from the Shop because they "know where the product comes from" (007). The Shop encourages fishers to travel to Bangkok on a monthly basis to sell their seafood at local farmers' market, enabling fishers to engage in conversation with consumers and tell of their fishing practices and way of life.

Consumers were also motivated by civic quality: wanting to provide support for local, small-scale fishers and arguing for "cutting the MP out of the system of seafood" (005) or wanting to support conservation efforts (i.e., "supporting responsible fishing" (003) and "ensuring that fishers use only big nets and do not catch small fish" (002). This merging of social concerns with environmental concerns is common, especially within sustainable food movements more generally (Olson, Clay,

---

[7] The sixth convention of inspirational quality is not drawn on (despite the rising profile of sustainable seafood in Asia) for it is not yet considered a significant factor influencing consumer choice for sustainable seafood in Thailand.

[8] These numbers refer to our key informant interviews, who were guaranteed confidentiality and anonymity. We entered our qualitative data into the software program NVivo.

and Pinto da Silva 2014). There is evidence that some consumers are motivated by opinion quality, for some interviewees referred to the views of marine activist Banjong Nasae when explaining their reasons for supporting the Shop (002, 003). As recipient of the 2015 Thai Social Enterprise award, the Shop has also gained public recognition for its commitment to social responsibility. One consumer learned about the Shop from the publicity garnered by this award; similarly, a piece in the Bangkok Post written about the Shop (Karnjanatawe 2015) has likely piqued the curiosity of potential buyers.

Industrial conventions do not yet have a direct influence over consumers who buy from the Shop: there is no certification scheme in place to justify market quality. However, in May 2016, it is anticipated that the Shop will release its Blue Brand standard. This tool will attest to the monitoring of supply chains and show consumers that the product they are purchasing has been caught by small-scale fishers using verifiable nondestructive fishing gear. The Blue Brand label will serve as a guarantee that the appropriate size of species is caught, that producers are involved in or supportive of community-based coastal resource conservation activities, and that the catching, preserving, processing, and packaging of Shop product is free from chemicals. Shop employees believe that this scheme will create a greater sense of legitimacy. Consumer survey participants also believe that this new label will allow seafood products to be sold at a higher price and might attract more consumers since the label acts as a guarantee of ecological sustainability.

Discussion

The Shop was established to source seafood from seven small-scale fisher groups in Prachuap Khiri Khan province: to a large extent the Shop has been able to meet this mandate. To sustain Shop sales, however, seafood needs to be sourced in a way that accounts for what can be caught locally and seasonally. Although the Shop sources small amounts of additional seafood from southern Thailand to meet specific consumer demands, this practice is labor intensive and less profitable than sourcing local products. Our analysis suggests that while a few consumers may demand a particular type of seafood product, different from what is being targeted by local fishers, the Shop should concentrate its effort in sourcing and processing local seafood. Lower trophic level fish such as short-bodied mackerel and goldstripe sardinella can be purchased from local fishers at a price premium while sustaining the Shop (in terms of revenue and in supporting its mandate to "go local").

In addition to these concerns, there are a few other challenges that the Shop faces, including seafood storage, ecological sustainability, shifting market relations, and long working hours of Shop employees. We expand on these issues below, since they are areas that the Shop must think through as it grows and expands.

Seafood storage

The Shop is constrained in terms of the volume of local seafood it can purchase. Local fishers only sell to the

Shop a few times per month; even then, they can only sell between 10 and 30 percent of their daily catch. Handling large volumes of seafood and seafood storage is therefore an issue for the Shop. Since the Shop, up until this point, has had limited storage capacity, fresh seafood has been cleaned and/or processed and then sold quickly to consumers. For direct sales to consumers, for example, the Shop sources seafood species in response to demand. Operating under a demand-driven business model, the Shop determines what seafood product consumers want and takes this information to fishers; if fishers cannot fill the order due to seasonality or low catch volume this is communicated back to the consumer. When last minute requests are made, fishers have often already sold their catch to a MP. Thus, there can be a mismatch between supply and demand.

The challenge with this model is that "the quantity of the fish is unpredictable": a fisher could catch 100 kg one day and more or less of the species the next day (013). One fisher explained how, "one time [he] had caught 200 kg of goldstripe sardinella but the Shop that day only wanted to buy 100 kg from [him]— hoping that tomorrow [he] would have another 100 kg to sell. The next day [he] didn't have 100 kg" (013). Some fishers felt that the Shop should not source according to consumer demand, rather that the Shop needs to promote what local fishers are catching and hence what is in season. Being able to handle greater volumes of seafood product through enhanced storage systems and more focused processing (i.e., concentrating on local main targeted species) will enable a larger percentage of fishers' catch to be purchased.

In December 2016, to address these challenges, the Shop moved operations to Khan Kradai village. Here the Shop is closer to the supply of local fish and is able to employ community members to assist with the workload (individuals can work when it is most convenient for them and be paid accordingly—they do not need to be employed part or full time). There are also plans to build a factory to enable employees to process and package products with greater efficiency. However, as one Shop staff member notes, this model will bring new challenges including getting the villagers involved in the processing so that the Shop becomes a "business for the community" (020). Nonetheless, this move may address some of the storage problems that the Shop faced in Year 1 of its operations.

Ecological sustainability

Ecological sustainability is an important component of the Shop's model and is of interest to fishers, Shop employees, and consumers. Fishers note that the Shop "provides a nontoxic aquatic product to consumers," ensures a "better environment," and in turn offers fishers "a higher price ... to have a better life" (013). While ecological sustainability is clearly valued (as per fishers' comments, the civic quality conventions, and the Shop's mandate), the Shop does not constantly carry out ecological monitoring. While the Shop has the equipment necessary to test products for chemicals for instance (including the sugar, fish sauce, and salt used in processing), Shop staff only test products when they initially buy from a fisher. After this, procurement is based on a system of trust.

Shop staff admitted that the NGO Thai Sea Watch Association had "promoted the use of legal gear within the [communities] first," before the Shop was established (019). Therefore, most local fishers who are selling to the Shop already engage in relatively ecologically sound fishing practices[9] and are often involved in conservation projects (e.g., constructing artificial reefs, crab banks, protecting seagrass beds, and not fishing in the immediate nearshore). Even so, fishers would appreciate further support in communicating the importance of protecting ocean ecology to consumers and the public more broadly. One fisher suggested that the Shop appoint at least one staff member to help with this transmission of knowledge. In this sense, fishers want "the Shop [not to] act only as a MP" (013), rather to be an advocate for ocean health too. Consumers too were interested to learn more "on the kinds of fish…and the Shop itself" (003) and to understand the seasonal schedule for species.

Shop consumers, in some cases, indicated that they consider their seafood purchases in terms of seasonality and trophic levels. For instance, when asked if they would purchase another kind of seafood if their preferred type was not available, over half of the consumers interviewed said that they would, since seasonality is important and "it is very hard to manage the Shop" (009). Unsure participants said that they would see what other fish was available and whether or not it is familiar; one participant said that she would "go to buy pork or chicken instead" (008). In terms of trophic levels, half of the consumers interviewed claimed to take this into consideration when purchasing seafood, explaining that they "don't like to buy species at top of food chain" (008) or prefer to "eat fish of small size because of less toxin" (007). One consumer even noted how "if you don't think about level of the food chain then it is not sustainable and will not leave [resources] for the next generation" (004). While many consumers we spoke with hold a surprising amount of knowledge on various ecological topics such as seasonality, bioaccumulation, and trophic levels, this was not the case across all Shop consumers nor is this likely the case across the general population.

Ensuring continuing seafood access

By purchasing seafood directly from fishers, the Shop is shifting market relations. Fishers have long been dependent upon close relationships with local MP. This relationship is linked with the quasi-credit system, whereby MP provide fishers with interest free monetary loans to support fishing-related activities (e.g., the buying of physical assets such as a fishing boat and

---

[9] Although there is no limit to the amount of gear used per fisher (which has clear sustainability implications), fishers note that they now use larger mesh sizes than before (2 cm originally) and that none of the fishers selling to the Shop use bottom trawls.

gear) and household activities (Bailey et al. 2016). In exchange for these services, fishers are often indebted or bonded to the MP, selling their product at a lower price, and prevented from selling their catch to another buyer.

A challenge for the Shop, as paying a price premium is reorganizing the value chain, is to interrupt these longstanding relationships without causing strife or removing the MP altogether (Bailey et al. 2016). This is especially important as the Shop can only source small volumes of seafood product, and fishers need to maintain their relationships with MP. Fishers who have *"kaew"*—a Thai word that describes the debt held with a MP—may be excluded from accessing the Shop. For example, several fishers with *"kaew"* said they could not sell their seafood to the Shop explaining that they must pay back the MP. Those fishers who could sell to the Shop indicated that this is because they either have no debt or because the MP they sell to knows of the Shop and allows them to sell a portion of their catch to the Shop. In areas where the Shop has a well-established presence, selling to the Shop may not be an issue given the small amount of seafood the Shop currently can source, yet fisher–MP relations will undoubtedly pose challenges as the Shop expands.

Intense working conditions of Shop employees

Shop employees work long hours and without overtime pay. Over the course of its first year of operation, the Shop has employed four—sometimes five—women. These women are responsible for everything from purchasing, processing,

and packaging seafood, to marketing, selling, and distributing products to consumers. We found the most labor intensive aspect of running the Shop is procuring and processing the seafood. The employee responsible for this described her average day as follows: (a) offloading boats and picking through fish (after dark, late into the evening); (b) cleaning and gutting fish to be ready for morning processing (starting at 2 or 3 am); and, (c) processing and packaging the fish with other workers (throughout the day). The late afternoon and early evening are the best time for this employee to sleep: most people could not manage these hours. Other staff face a similarly significant workload. The Shop manager, for instance, is in charge of finding markets, connecting with the consumer, managing public relations, supervising the work of other employees, and is now also responsible for developing the Blue Brand label that Shop products will soon be sold under.

Year 1 of any business venture is labor intensive, and this is reflected in talking with Shop employees. However, as the Shop becomes more established and hopefully with the name recognition that should come with the Blue Brand label, things will become easier. Working conditions would also be enhanced for employees if the Shop were to emphasize local seafood and concentrate their efforts on processing just a few key species. At this point, our analysis suggests that the Shop does not have the labor to handle individual consumer requests for specific types of seafood products and for species not found in Prachuap Khiri Khan province.

Conclusion

The Fisherfolk Shop is an example of an initiative designed to support local seafood. Small-scale fishers are encouraged to fish (or continue fishing) in ecologically sustainable ways, with the Shop connecting this seafood caught with consumers who want to support such practices through purchasing power (Olson, Clay, and Pinto da Silva 2014). By creating an emerging niche market, the Shop can pay small-scale fishers a premium for their seafood, offering more than an average MP. The Shop relies on short value chains and relatively wealthy, urban consumers in Bangkok who are willing to pay more for sustainable seafood to sustain this model. Consumers are found to be motivated by health and food safety when it comes to supporting sustainable seafood, but there is clearly a concern for other ethical issues like social justice and ecological health. Among consumers purchasing from the Shop, there is a substantial amount of support for such a sustainable seafood initiative.

What an analysis of Year 1 of the Shop's operations suggests is that there is an urban market for seafood caught by small-scale fishers in Prachuap Khiri Khan province. Top Shop revenue generators include mackerel (Indo-Pacific king mackerel and short-bodied mackerel), blue swimming crab, and banana shrimp—all local species. From a revenue generating and labor-savings perspective, the Shop could benefit greatly from concentrating its' efforts on processing and marketing these local species rather than purchasing small amounts of seafood from southern Thailand to meet consumer demand. The Shop would also do well to consider what kinds of value-added products make sense from a time and economic perspective. Fishers, their families, or members of their community could do more of this processing, as evidence shows that the Shop is able to make significant revenue by buying and selling these already processed seafood products. Given the large volume of unprocessed local fish the Shop sold in Year 1, and the decent profits that ensued, there are also clear advantages to promoting this side of the business. An active education campaign could help raise consumer awareness of the benefits of "going local."

What has been found with organic and related foods is that branded products in supermarkets enables access to middle-class consumers who are willing to pay premiums (Ponte 2016): our article explores if this can be leveraged for sustainable seafood as well. Our insights suggest that this might be the case in Thailand, although time will tell. Questions to consider include assessing whether consumer purchasing behavior in the general public would reproduce a merging of social and environmental concerns, and whether the general Thai public is even thinking about sustainable, local seafood. Certainly the Shop offers a seafood product that is in stark contrast to the labor abuse and ecological challenges facing the off-shore sector (Marschke and Vandergeest 2016). The Shop initiative, although unintended, is quite timely in this sense. As such, there are many reasons to be cautiously optimistic about this approach to creating an alternative market for seafood caught by small-scale fishers that supports local sustainability.

Acknowledgments

This article has been written as part of the research program: New Directions in Environmental Governance (NDEG). The authors thank fishers, shop employees, and consumers who generously took their time to participate in this research. Thanks to Iftekharul Haque and Dr. Gordon Betcherman for their support in analyzing buying and selling data. They also thank participants at CCSEAS 2015 in Ottawa, Canada and at the WFP conference in Bangkok, Thailand for their feedback, along with anonymous reviewers. The authors gratefully acknowledge the financial support provided by the Social Sciences and Humanities Research Council (SSHRC).

References

Bailey, Megan, Simon Bush, Peter Oosterveer, and Laksmi Larastiti. 2016. "Fishers, Fair Trade, and Finding Middle Ground." *Fisheries Research*. In Press, Corrected Proof — Note to users. 10 pages. doi:10.1016/j.fishres.2015.11.027.

Belton, Ben, and Shakuntala Haraksingh Thilsted. 2014. "Fisheries in Transition: Food and Nutrition Security Implications for the Global South." *Global Food Security* 3 (1): 59–66. doi:10.1016/j.gfs.2013.10.001.

Belton, Ben, and Simon R Bush. 2014. "Beyond Net Deficits: New Priorities for an Aquacultural Geography: Beyond Net Deficits." *The Geographical Journal* 180 (1): 3–14. doi:10.1111/geoj.12035.

Blackmore, Emma, and Hannah Norbury. 2015. *What's the Catch? Lessons from and Prospects for the Marine Stewardship Council Certification in Developing Countries.* London: International Institute for Environment and Development.

Boltanski, Luc, and Thévenot, Laurent. 1991. *De la Justification: Les Économies de la Grandeur.* Paris: Gallimard (NRF Essais).

Bush, Simon R., et al. 2013. "Certify Sustainable Aquaculture." *Science* 341 (6150): 1067–1068.

Campbell, Alissa M, and Rod MacRae. 2013. "Local Food Plus: The Connective Tissue in Local/sustainable Supply Chain Development." *Local Environment* 18 (5): 557–566. doi:10.1080/13549839.2013.788488.

Evans, David. 2011. "Consuming Conventions: Sustainable Consumption, Ecological Citizenship and the Worlds of Worth." *Journal of Rural Studies* 27 (2): 109–115. doi:10.1016/j.jrurstud.2011.02.002.

Food and Agriculture Organization. 2014. *State of World Fisheries and Aquaculture 2014.* Rome, Italy: Food & Agriculture Organization of the United Nations.

Hallstein, Eric, and Sofia B. Villas-Boas. 2013. "Can Household Consumers Save the Wild Fish? Lessons from a Sustainable Seafood Advisory." *Journal of Environmental Economics and Management* 66 (1): 52–71. doi:10.1016/j.jeem.2013.01.003.

Jacquet, Jennifer, et al. 2010. "Conserving Wild Fish in a Sea of Market-Based Efforts." *Oryx* 44 (01): 45. doi:10.1017/S0030605309990470.

Jacquet, Jennifer L., and Daniel Pauly. 2007. "The Rise of Seafood Awareness Campaigns in an Era of Collapsing Fisheries." *Marine Policy* 31 (3): 308–313. doi:10.1016/j.marpol.2006.09.003.

Karnjanatawe, Karnjana. 2015. "Fishing for Ethical Business." *Bangkok Post*. http://www.bangkokpost.com/lifestyle/social-and-lifestyle/662872/fishing-for-ethical-business (accessed November 10 2015).

Kelly, Matthew, Sam-ang Seubsman, Cathy Banwell, Jane Dixon, and Adrian Sleigh. 2015. "Traditional, Modern or Mixed? Perspectives on Social, Economic, and Health Impacts of Evolving Food Retail in Thailand." *Agriculture and Human Values* 32 (3): 445–460. doi:10.1007/s10460-014-9561-z.

Konefal, Jason. 2013. "Environmental Movements, Market-Based Approaches, and Neoliberalization: A Case Study of the Sustainable Seafood Movement." *Organization & Environment* 26 (3): 336–352.

Lay, Kaitlan. 2012. "Seafood Ecolabels: For Whom and to What Purpose?" Dalhousie *Journal of Interdisciplinary Management* 8 (2): 1-22. doi:10.5931/djim.v8i2.211.

Marine Stewardship Council. 2014. "MSC Fisheries Certification Requirements and Guidance, Version 2." https://www.msc.org/documents/scheme-documents/fisheries-certification-scheme-documents/fisheries-certification-requirements-version-2.0.

Marschke, Melissa, and Peter Vandergeest. 2016. "Slavery Scandals: Unpacking Labour Challenges and Policy Responses within the off-Shore Fisheries Sector." *Marine Policy* 68 (June): 39–46. doi:10.1016/j.marpol.2016.02.009.

Migliore, Giuseppina, Giorgio Schifani, and Luigi Cembalo. 2015. "Opening the Black Box of Food Quality in the Short Supply Chain: Effects of Conventions of Quality on Consumer Choice." *Food Quality and Preference* 39 (January): 141–146. doi:10.1016/j.foodqual.2014.07.006.

Olson, Julia, Patricia M. Clay, and Patricia Pinto da Silva. 2014. "Putting the Seafood in Sustainable Food Systems." *Marine Policy* 43 (January): 104–111. doi:10.1016/j.marpol.2013.05.001.

Parkes, Graeme, et al. 2010. "Behind the Signs—A Global Review of Fish Sustainability Information Schemes." *Reviews in Fisheries Science* 18 (4): 344–356. doi:10.1080/10641262.2010.516374.

Ponte, Stefano. 2012. "The Marine Stewardship Council (MSC) and the Making of a Market for 'sustainable Fish.'" *Journal of Agrarian Change* 12 (2-3): 300–315.

Ponte, Stefano. 2016. "Convention Theory in the Anglophone Agro-Food Literature: Past, Present and Future." *Journal of Rural Studies* 44 (April): 12–23. doi:10.1016/j.jrurstud.2015.12.019.

Ponte, Stefano, and Timothy Sturgeon. 2014. "Explaining Governance in Global Value Chains: A Modular Theory-Building Effort." *Review of International Political Economy* 21 (1): 195–223. doi:10.1080/09692290.2013.809596.

Posri, Wilatsana, Bhavani Shankar, and Supatra Chadbunchachai. 2006. "Consumer Attitudes Towards and Willingness to Pay for Pesticide Residue Limit Compliant 'Safe' Vegetables in Northeast Thailand." *Journal of International Food & Agribusiness Marketing* 19 (1): 81–101. doi:10.1300/J047v19n01_05.

Roheim, Cathy A. 2009. "An Evaluation of Sustainable Seafood Guides: Implications for Environmental Groups and the Seafood Industry." *Marine Resource Economics* 24 (3): 301–310.

Roitner-Schobesberger, Birgit, Ika Darnhofer, Suthichai Somsook, and Christian R. Vogl. 2008. "Consumer Perceptions of Organic Foods in Bangkok, Thailand." *Food Policy* 33 (2): 112–121. doi:10.1016/j.foodpol.2007.09.004.

Sangkumchaliang, Parichard, and W. Huang. 2012a. "Consumers' Perceptions and Attitudes of Organic Food Products in Northern Thailand." *International Food and Agribusiness Management Review* 15 (1): 87–102.

Sangkumchaliang, Parichard, and W. Huang. 2012b. "Consumers' Perceptions and Attitudes of Organic Food Products in Northern Thailand." *International Food and Agribusiness Management Review* 15 (1): 87–102.

Srithamma, S., J. Vithayarungruangsri, and T. Posayanonda. 2005. "Food Safety Programme: A Key Component for Health Promotion." (accessed January 21, 2010).

Vandergeest, Peter. 2007. "Certification and Communities: Alternatives for Regulating the Environmental and Social Impacts of Shrimp Farming." *World Development* 35 (7): 1152–1171. doi:10.1016/j.worlddev.2006.12.002.

Vandergeest, Peter, Stefano Ponte, and Simon R Bush. 2015. "Assembling Sustainable Territories: Space, Subjects, Objects, and Expertise in Seafood Certification." *Environment and Planning* A 47: 1907–1925. doi:10.1177/0308518X15599297.

What's Old Is New Again: Innovative Policies to Support Thai Fresh Markets Within a Healthy Food System

Cathy Banwell[A], Jane Dixon[A], Matthew Kelly[B], Sam-ang Seubsman[C], Wimalin Rimpeekool[A] & Adrian Sleigh[B]

Traditionally, Thais have bought their food from fresh markets. However, recently multi-national supermarket chains have expanded rapidly so that currently, Thais procure food from both modern and traditional retail formats. If Thailand were to follow the Western pattern, supermarkets will become the dominant food retail format.

We present a synthesis of 10 years of multidisciplinary research, examining the contribution of food retail to the Thai nutrition and health transition, to demonstrate that fresh markets provide access to fresh, affordable, nutritious foods. Fresh market shoppers have healthier diets and lower chronic disease risks than other groups.

In the South East Asia context, the protection of fresh markets constitutes a novel intervention to protect and promote nutrition-sensitive retail. This could be achieved through policy action nationally, with monitoring of national and multi-national supermarket chain growth, regionally, with planning to safeguard fresh markets' urban locations, and locally, with the development of food hubs.

***Keywords**: food system, nutrition-sensitive agriculture, food retail, nutrition transition, Thailand*

[A] National Centre for Epidemiology & Population Health, The Research School of Population Health, ANU College of Medicine, Biology and Environment, The Australian National University.

[B] Department of Global Health, The Research School of Population Health, ANU College of Medicine, Biology and Environment, The Australian National University.

[C] School of Human Ecology, Sukhothai Thammathirat Open University.

doi: 10.18278/wfp.2.2.3.1.4

Background

Three major and interrelated shifts in theorizing food systems have been underway over the last two decades. They are as follows: recognition that food security requires the provision of healthy as well as plentiful food; evidence of a nutrition transition linking over rather than under-nutrition to some of the top ten health burdens in much of the world (Popkin, Horton, and Kim 2001; WHO 2014); and recent acknowledgement that more attention should be paid to the connection between agriculture and nutritional food, otherwise known as nutrition-sensitive agriculture (Jaenicke and Virchow 2013). These shifts have occurred in the context of rapid urbanization in economically transitioning regions and countries.

As urbanization has increased rapidly across the economically developing world a burgeoning need has arisen to recognize the vital role of food systems in supplying the appetites of urban populations. Increasingly, it is understood that urban settings are intricate and not only require, but also encourage the development of complex food systems to provide food and nutrition security. Cities are "drivers of the global food system" because they are where most of the population lives and the needs of urban populations promote demand at a sufficient scale and for novel products. However, urban agglomerations have become mainly sites of consumption with food production and other functions of the food system remaining invisible to most consumers (Dansero, Pettenati, and Toldo 2015). Indeed, the modern food system has

being characterized by a disconnection between producers, suppliers, and consumers; the dis-embedding of food from its place of production, and related values and identities; and the dis-entwining of food-related spheres of economy and life such as food, care, education, and leisure (Wiskerke 2009).

The food system itself consists of multiple elements including production, processing, transport, consumption, and waste management at which interventions can modify or improve the amount and type of food that reaches consumers. As Ingram (2011; 2013) and others have noted, the food system underpins food security with the latter predicated upon the proposition that individuals and households have access to food, either through their own production or, as in the case of most urban consumers, because adequate nutrition for healthy development and growth is accessible, affordable, and acceptable through the market place.

A conceptual gap exists between theories about the transition from under- to over-nutrition and the concept of food security which was developed mainly by those concerned with under-nutrition (Popkin 2014). A broader concept of food and nutrition security is now required to address a problem developing in even the poorest parts of the world, namely that of over-nutrition. While obesity is commonly seen as a disease of affluence related to overconsumption, it is increasingly recognized that poorer populations within wealthy societies are increasingly likely to be overweight and obese. In poorer countries, the rural and urban poor can be obese and remain malnourished because their diets consist of inexpensive foods lacking essential micro-nutrients. A contributing factor is the penetration of industrial food systems and their retailing arms that have increased the affordability and availability of ultra-processed foods. Rather than populations eating "whole foods," increasing volumes of grains, meats, dairy, fruit, and vegetables are being transformed into processed foods requiring the addition of salts, fat, and sugars to make them palatable. For some staple foods—breads and grains—nutrients are being removed during processing (Winson 2013).

Recognition of this trend to more accessible processed food is evident in the move to understand and develop nutrition-sensitive agriculture which aims to encourage increasing consumption of fresh fruits and vegetables and decrease consumption of unhealthy ultra-processed foods (Hawkesworth et al. 2010). Agriculture is only one of the domains contributing to the food supply with food retail playing another important, but under-researched, component. Modern retailers—supermarket chains, fast food chains, and food service conglomerates—operate upstream through their supply chain contracts purchasing foods containing required marketable qualities and downstream through shaping the accessibility, affordability, and acceptability of food. In this domain, they influence consumer demand by shaping food preferences, as well as purchasing and preparation practices, and they bear the major responsibility for distributing calories and nutrients and hence consumer health outcomes. In other words, a food system that is nutrition-sensitive requires nutrition-sensitive retail formats.

As food systems have become globalized, fresh and processed foods from around the world are made available and affordable in an increasing number of transitioning countries. This nutrition outcome, a positive development in some countries and not in others, has been made possible largely due to the logistics capabilities of modern retailers. Retailers do not work in isolation but amplify the changes in what is being produced and processed. They do this by playing a major role in product formulation and specifications. This is particularly so in terms of their home brand categories, which can make up between 30% and 60% of supermarket processed goods. Retailer-led supply chains can foster the adoption of agricultural practices which reduce the diversity of food produced on individual farms and in regions: a prime example being their demand for sweet pepper (Schipmann and Qaim 2010) as happened in Thailand some years back.

The consequences of contracts to expand the supply of particular foods for agricultural environments are of interest in terms of the food and nutrition security of future generations. Elsewhere, it has been argued that supermarkets are part of the general trend in agro-business toward agricultural intensification, environmental pollution, and a reduction of agro-biodiversity (Wiskerke 2009). The agro-business model involves the company in food production practices through particular contract-based procurement systems. In "direct procurement" systems, suppliers and retailers have a modest input into producer practices but can influence "cultivation methods including the amount of agrochemicals input" (Endo 2014). Under contract farming, retailers or large suppliers exert more control over the entire cultivation process (Endo 2014).

Within any food supply, priority should be given to the availability of a variety of foods, because a varied diet optimizes health and reduces morbidity (Walquist, Lo, and Myers 1989; Ogle, Hung, and Tuyet 2001). "Maintenance of the variety of food is, in turn, dependent on the maintenance of biodiversity" (Walquist, Lo, and Myers 2012). This principle requires policies which support the sustainability of the bio-regional characteristics of local food systems. In summary, it is important to understand the supermarket revolution as it "cut[s] across the entire economy" and that "understand[ing] the impact of supermarkets presents serious analytical *and* policy challenges" (Timmer 2009).

For many centuries, fresh markets have played a key role in the bio-economies of rural Thailand and they continue to play a role in providing the population with fresh produce that is both diverse and has been sustainable up till now. Protecting fresh markets and their supply chains through policy initiatives can provide a mechanism for supporting a healthy food system so that Thais continue to easily access affordable, healthy, culturally acceptable foods.

Thailand's Retail Transition

Thailand's recent history exemplifies these major nutrition and retail transitions. Food retail has traditionally been via fresh markets, although the country has stood out in South East Asian for its rapid transition to supermarkets (Mutebi 2007; Shannon 2009). Supermarkets first appeared in Bangkok in the 1960s and rapidly spread to other cities and rural areas following a well-defined pattern (Kelly et al. 2015). This spread was facilitated by partnerships between foreign owned and Thai firms. During the financial crisis of 1997, these relationships were dissolved and transnational food companies, mainly European in origin, proceeded to massively expand their operations along with Thailand's own Chaoren Pokphan, the market leader in this category, and the Siam Makkro chain (Tokrisna 2007; USDA 2000). The supermarket expansion was accompanied by an annual loss of around 25,000 small retailers (Hawkes 2008). New legislation in the 2000s slowed the growth of foreign owned supermarkets somewhat, but they nevertheless continue to spread, along with convenience stores (Banwell et al. 2013; Endo 2013). As a result, the number of fresh markets has declined nationally, falling from 160 to 50 in the past decade in Bangkok alone (Sriangura and Sakseree 2009).

This article reports on a synthesis of a number of studies conducted in Thailand by the research team over a 10 year period starting in 2005. During this time, the team has addressed a number of research questions including: how has food retail changed in Thailand, how are fresh markets responding to the growth in supermarkets; who is using these different food retail formats and why, and what effect is the food retail transition having on population diets and health risks? In this article, we synthesize findings from these studies to examine the contribution of food retail, as a central element of the food system, to the Thai nutrition and health transition. We propose that the recognition of nutrition-sensitive agriculture demands greater support from nutrition planners for nutrition-sensitive retail (fresh markets) because they distribute nutrition-sensitive produce.

Methodology

This article draws upon on a 10 year research program that includes ethnographic case studies of three fresh markets in the central region around Bangkok, two markets in Chiang Mai in the North, one in Khon Kaen (the North East), and two in Nakhon Sri Thammarat in the southern region. All studies by a team of Australian and Thai researchers included observations at markets, informal interviews with shoppers, focus groups discussions with stallholders, and a brief face-to-face survey. A detailed description of methods is provided in Banwell et al. (2013).

In addition, a large cohort study conducted in Thailand (the Thai Cohort Study (TCS)) (Sleigh et al. 2007) provided a population for a smaller survey conducted in 2012 on food purchasing and consumption. A post-code defined, sub-sample of members from the TCS was drawn. They were urban residents from the four major regions of Thailand where the food retail ethnographic case studies were conducted. Detailed questionnaires collecting data on the food retail environment, shopping behavior, and food consumption were returned by 1,516 cohort members (45% response rate). Using these data, respondents were categorized into modern shoppers (supermarkets and convenience stores), mainly traditional (fresh markets), and mixed (equal use). An additional group of questionnaire respondents from two regions were selected for face-to-face, in-depth interviews to "flesh out" the quantitative information gathered. A detailed description of the research methods and findings is provided in Kelly et al. (2014).

Findings

Fresh markets and supermarkets: products, consumers, and locations

As their name suggests, fresh markets sell mainly fresh produce: vegetables, fruit, raw meats, and live animals, including insects and reptiles (Dixon et al. 2007). In addition, they sometimes offer sweets, bakery goods, and staples such as bags of rice, fermented and preserved products, and cooked foods, for the plastic bag housewife to take home for the family (Yasmeen 2000). Many stall holders are women with stalls run as family businesses. Despite some basic similarities, fresh markets may vary in their size, location, their infrastructure, and their range of products. They provide locally grown as well as imported fruit and vegetables, and products that are suitable for regional cuisines and attuned to local festivals and other cultural activities (Banwell et al. 2013). In addition, they are often conveniently located in urban centers, easily accessible on foot or on motorcycles, and they sell food affordably and in small quantities suitable for daily shoppers to carry home. They are valued because they offer the opportunity to develop personalized relationships between stall holders and consumers, so that shoppers can seek reduced prices and detailed information on the provenance of produce.

Supermarkets and hypermarkets until recently have been mainly located on the outskirts of towns, and therefore accessible and convenient to those who own cars, which is an increasing segment of the Thai population. Results from the 2012 survey, described earlier, have shown that over a 10 year period the proportion of the sample who had access to a supermarket increased from 47% to 85% (Kelly et al. 2014). Urban residents, those who owned a bicycle or motorcycle and those who received lower incomes were more likely than others to purchase fresh produce mainly at fresh markets. Supermarkets sell fresh fruit and vegetables that are often better quality but more expensive than fresh markets (Schipmann and Qaim 2011). Mainly, though, their sales consist of less healthy, packaged, and highly processed goods.

Impacts of food retail on diets and health

The 2012 Thai Cohort Sub-Study demonstrated that those who mainly used modern retail formats, such as supermarkets and convenience stores, had a higher consumption of unhealthy foods such as soft drinks, snack foods, processed meats, western style bakery goods, instant foods, and deep fried foods. Those who shopped mainly at fresh markets had a higher consumption of vegetables (Kelly et al. 2014).

Table 1 reveals associations between food shopping patterns measured in the 2012 sub-study, and their diet and health outcomes in 2013 recorded as part of the main Thai Cohort Study. Those who shopped more at supermarkets had higher risk of having poor diets, measured by fast food, soft drink, instant foods, and deep fried food consumption frequency. They were also more likely to consume insufficient amounts of fruit and vegetables and to have been diagnosed as having hyperlipidemia and ischemic heart disease. Although not statistically significant, the figures point to this group being more overweight or obese and more likely to have gained weight in the 2 years between surveys.

Discussion

This mixed methods research, conducted over a number of years, confirms the importance of fresh markets to the supply of local, fresh foods, and foods from near-neighbor countries, sold at prices affordable for poorer segments of the Thai population. Our data show that those who shop at them are less likely to purchase unhealthy, highly processed foods and more likely to purchase local, as well as imported, vegetables and fruit. This has implications for nutrition-sensitive agriculture as local fresh foods can improve nutritional status (Ogle et al. 2001) because they are bio-nutritionally diverse (Ruel 2003) and they are environmentally adapted to local conditions. While supermarkets may increase diet diversity in some settings, such as disadvantaged neighborhoods in urban USA (Reardon 2011), in Thailand, where fresh markets remain popular, supermarkets do not usually provide an equally broad range of local products.

Supermarkets can contribute to population weight gain through the sale of sugar-sweetened beverages, and other highly processed, inexpensive foods that are major "vectors" of sugar, fat, and salt in transitioning Asian countries (Baker and Friel 2014). Major food processing companies have been shown to increase their profits by making and selling processed rather than unprocessed foods (Stuckler and Nestle 2012). Internationally, supermarkets are implicated in over-nutrition and micro-nutrient deficiencies in lower middle income countries (LMIC) (Gomez and Ricketts 2013). The evidence is mixed however, with an association between supermarket shopping and unhealthy food consumption observed in Guatamala (Asfaw 2008) but not in Tunisia (Tessier et al. 2008). In Indonesia, supermarket shopping is associated with overweight and obesity in children living in high income households but not in adults (Umberger et al. 2014). In contrast in Kenya, supermarket shopping was associated with unhealthier weight in adults but reduced underweight in children and may be related to consumers' initial nutritional status (Qaim et al. 2014).

The precautionary principle is used to invoke the prevention of harms to health even when the evidence of risks is inconclusive and it has been advocated in response to the influence of multi-national food companies (Stuckler and Nestle 2012). It can also be applied to the effects of large national and international food businesses as they influence food producer decisions and their cultivation practices. In the case of the food retail transition, application of the precautionary principle would support the protection of alternative sources of fresh food, rather than allowing food purchasing to become concentrated by a few conglomerates which offer less healthy retail environments. It is particularly relevant in this context because, although the diets of those purchasing at modern retail formats are likely to be less healthy than those of traditional food markets shoppers, poor health outcomes take time to appear.

International research indicates that the dietary and health effects of the transition to supermarkets depends greatly on the pre-existing food system and on broader social, economic, and political conditions, such as urbanization, sedentary working conditions, car-reliance, and increasing female employment among others. Nevertheless, the food retail system is influential; the Thai population has gained weight (Aekplakorn 2011) as the number of modern food retail outlets, including convenience stores, has risen (Kelly et al. 2010). Thai supermarkets reached annual compound growth rates of 16% between 2001 and 2009 (Reardon et al. 2012), and packaged foods from modern retail have increased in sales by 65% over 15 years (Ng and Dunford 2013).

In modern western countries supermarket growth has been linked to a decline in small farms, and the growth of agri-business which has come to dominate food retail (Wiskerke 2009). Thailand's major supermarket chains are using many of the same strategies as those adopted by Western supermarkets to capture market power (Dixon and Banwell 2015). Currently, supermarkets in Thailand procure fresh produce in two ways: from large-scale agricultural companies and from small farmers (Endo 2014). However, supermarkets prefer to source from larger farmers who have considerable existing assets, such as education, and access to roads, water, and electricity (Andersson et al. 2015) which "poses a challenge to asset-poor farmers" (Reardon 2011).

The welfare and health of small farmers in Thailand has rarely been considered in the analysis of the transition (Sriboonchitta and Wiboonpoongse 2008). Some farmers may be financially better off supplying under contract (Sriboonchitta and Wiboonpoongse 2008) to large agribusiness and supermarket chains while others, particularly smaller, less asset-endowed farmers, can be economically excluded from the economic benefits associated with supermarket growth (Timmer 2009) and their financial and food security threatened. For example, Kenyan farmers who supplied to modern food retail were better off financially than those who did not, but many who entered this channel were not able to maintain the supply and dropped out after several years (Andersson et al. 2015). In South Africa, fresh markets are still the most important outlets for small farmers even though they have been largely replaced by supermarket chains (McLachlan and Landman 2013). Participation by small farmers in supermarket supply chains can also shift power from men to women within households (Qaim et al. 2014). Overall, supplying to large supermarket chains can increase inequality among farm producers leading small producers to relinquish their farms and join the mass movement of rural poor into

the urban centers. As noted already, supermarkets can have a negative impact on the agricultural environment (Wiskerke 2009) through their influence on cultivation methods and control over the cultivation process (Endo 2014).

In countries, such as China, and some South East Asian nations supermarkets have been viewed as "tools of modernization" (Reardon 2011) and in Vietnam as a vehicle to improve food safety standards (Wertheim-Heck, Vellema, and Spaargaren 2015). However, given that fresh markets can play an important function in providing healthy, fresh, affordable, and potentially more sustainable food within the food system, policies are required to support their continued existence in the face of considerable economic power residing in large national and international food retailers. The precautionary principle suggests that there is a role for policies to support and protect fresh markets for the benefits of consumers' health and well-being at different levels.

Thai national food policy toward nutrition-sensitive retail

Asian governments' policy responses to the supermarket revolution have been described in the following terms: "where there have been regulations to slow growth (such as in Thailand, Indonesia, and Malaysia) they have been vacillating, partially implemented, and side-stepped by local interactions and co-opting of traditional retail, or format diversification, or both" (Reardon et al. 2014). In other words, more could be done in these countries to control the growth and spread of supermarkets.

Thailand has been cognizant of the need for policies to encourage nutrition-sensitive agriculture (Tontisirin et al. 2013) particularly in light of the government's aim to reduce overweight, obesity, and associated non-communicable diseases (NCDs). Despite public health campaigns, there has been little sign of success in preventing population weight gain and growth of NCDs. Consequently, in 2008, a National Food Committee was established to strengthen food management, efficiency, and effectiveness across agencies to "create momentum from agriculture to food, nutrition, and health" (Tontisirin et al. 2013). However, government action plans to combat overweight, obesity, and NCDs do not explicitly recognize or address the role of food retail in the transition to over-nutrition. The Thai Strategic Framework for Food Management connects agricultural production to health through food and nutrition (Tontisirin et al. 2013) using a food chain approach but again food retail is not discussed. This points to a need for the national food policy to recognize and address food retail as a site for intervention to safeguard Thai diets and maintain a diverse diet.

Regional and community level planning

There is a view that urban and regional planning could do considerably more to build more sustainable urban food environments (Wiskerke 2009; Dixon and Ballantyne-Brodie 2015). Due to their historical role as the major source of food for urban populations Thai fresh markets are often easily accessible for consumers throughout urban centers with their location key to their continuing success.

A pressure on centrally located fresh markets derives from population and transport systems growth. With increasing affluence, Thai car ownership and usage has become widespread (Berecki-Gisoli et al. 2015). Fresh markets, located in pedestrian accessible locations, may be moved or removed so that they do not obstruct the flow of commuter traffic. As cities become more car orientated, consumers will choose to purchase larger quantities of food in supermarkets with car parks on the outskirts of cities, leading people to higher exposure to unhealthy food in them. Furthermore, if fresh markets are to remain viable they need to be easily accessible to the farmers and suppliers who deliver produce in bulk. All these factors demand that careful planning for the location of fresh markets is required to protect them into the future.

The Thai government in the early to mid-2000s placed restrictions on the growth of foreign retailers often at the behest of small to middle-sized retailers and has taken other steps more recently but seems to have failed to curb their spread. Government restrictions, via site plan regulations, have limited the size of new stores, prompting large international retailers like Tesco to open large numbers of smaller stores leading to vocal opposition from local small retailers (Endo 2013). The vigorous lobbying and discussion about regulations concerning issues such as store size, location, and trading hours are testament to the importance of these features for the overall success of food retailing formats at the community level and citizen disquiet suggests that Thai government should continue to monitor and to implement regulations. At present, it appears that the major policy consideration in these discussions is the economic survival of small to medium-sized retailers in the face of large transnational and national companies. The potential health effects of a supermarket revolution do not seem to have been considered.

Food hubs

Food hubs have been advocated as a way of integrating small producers into the supply chains of large supermarkets by "bringing the market to the farmer" (Reardon, Timmer, and Minten 2012, 12336) and providing them with access to financial and other services as well as collection points for fresh food close to where it is produced. In countries like India, they have mainly been used to help small farmers' access supermarket supply chains (Reardon, Timmer, and Minten 2012). They are a growing feature of US and Australian food systems. These forms of assistance would be useful to small farmers producing for fresh markets.

In the west, food hubs have been proposed as an alternative channel for making fresh produce accessible to a population that is seeking an alternative to globalized, mass-produced food. Such alternatives often have taken the form of direct transactions between producers and consumers. In this context, food hubs are understood "as networks and intersections of grassroots, community-based organizations and individuals that work together to build increasingly socially just, economically robust, and ecologically sound food systems that connect farmers with consumers as

directly as possible" (Blay-Palmer et al. 2013). In this manifestation, food hubs are part of alternative food networks (AFN), a growing movement that aims to by-pass the industrialized food system. Like western AFNs, Thai fresh markets have short food supply chains in the main and provide opportunities for the operation of regard and trust between vendors and consumers in the retail relationships. However, Thai fresh markets do not draw as heavily upon "ecological characteristics" such as organic or non-genetically modified produce in the same way that European AFNs do (Renting, Marsden, and Banks 2003), although there are limited moves in this direction. In contrast to the AFN movement in the west, Thai fresh markets have not emerged as a radical movement combating an established globalizing, industrialized food system (Goodwin 2003). Instead, they represent a traditional food supply network that is attempting to survive in the face of an increasingly industrialized food system. In the west, food hubs are being proposed as a tool for scaling up from farmers' markets although they struggle to maintain economic viability (Cleveland et al. 2014). However, in Thailand, many wholesale and fresh markets already operate somewhat similarly to a food hub. What is required to operate fully as a food hub is improved economic, physical, and organization structures to enable small producers to continue in production outside the major supermarket supply chains. Having viable produce supplies means that fresh markets can continue to compete with the new supermarket supply chains.

Conclusion

Thailand is taking impressive action to monitor and respond to increasing overweight and obesity through the work of the newly formed National Food Committee (Chavasit, Kasemsup, and Tontisirin 2013). However, relatively little is known still about the nutrition and health effects of evolving food retail environments in SE Asia, including Thailand, particularly in relation to the growing health-related problem of obesity. What is needed is new and additional information on how food retail changes affect farm enterprise and environmental sustainability through upstream influences on production and processing and downstream effects on individuals and households through food purchasing, diets and related social practices, according to socio-economic and other characteristics. Ultimately, more targeted and more multi-sectorial policy interventions upstream and downstream are required.

Western experience suggests that protecting fresh markets has the potential to safeguard consumer dietary diversity, the provision of affordable, accessible foods and the maintenance of short food chains and hence the viability of local food producers. In a rapidly globalizing world, the shift to supermarkets as the main purveyors of food has been described as the supermarket revolution. It is seen as an inevitable consequence of globalization and modernization. However, it is possible for national and local governments to consciously protect fresh markets if they are understood as the food retail component of a nutrition-sensitive agricultural system.

Acknowledgments

This study was part of the Thai Health-Risk Transition research program supported by the International Collaborative Research Grants Scheme with joint grants from the Wellcome Trust UK (GR071587MA) and the Australian NHMRC (268055). We thank the Thai Cohort Study team for their support without which this work would not be possible.

References

Aekplakorn, Wichai. 2011. Report on the Thai National Health Examination Survey 2008–09. Nonthaburi: National Health Examination Survey Office.

Andersson, Camilla, Christine Chege, Elizaphran Rao, and Matin Qaim. 2015. "Following Up On Smallholder farmers and supermarkets in Kenya." *American Journal of Agricultural Economics*. doi: 10.1093/ajae/aav006.

Asfaw, Abay. 2008. "Does supermarket purchase affect the dietary practices of households? Some empirical evidence from Guatamala." *Development Policy Review* 26 (2):227-243.

Baker, Phillip, and Sharon Friel. 2014. "Processed foods and the nutrition transition: evidence from Asia." *Obesity Reviews* 15 (7):564-577.

Banwell, Cathy, Jane Dixon, Sam-Ang Seubsman, S. Pangsap, and Matthew Kelly. 2013. "Evolving food retail environments in Thailand and implications for the health and nutrition transition." *Public Health Nutrition* 16 (4):608-615.

Berecki-Gisoli, Jannecke, Vasoontara Yiengprugsawn, Matthew Kelly, Rod McClure, Sam-ang Seubsman, Adrian Sleigh, and The Thai Cohort Study Team. 2015. "The Impact of the Thai motorcycle transition on road traffic injury: Thai Cohort Study results." *PLOS One* 10(3): (3). doi: e0120617. doi:10.1371/journal.

Blay-Palmer, Alison, Karen Landman, Irena Knezevic, and Ryan Hayhurst. 2013. "Constructing resilient, transformative communities through sustainable "food hubs"." *Local Environment: The International Journal of Justice and Sustainability* 18 (5):521-528.

Chavasit, V., V. Kasemsup, and K. Tontisirin. 2013. "Thailand conquered undernutrition very successfully but has not slowed obesity." *Obesity Reviews*. doi: doi: 10.1111/obr.12091.

Cleveland, D., N. Muller, A. Tranovich, N. Mazaroli, and K. Hinson. 2014. "Local food hubs for alternative food systems: A case study from Santa Barbara County, California." *Journal of Rural Studies* 35:26-36.

Dansero, W., G. Pettenati, and A. Toldo. 2015. "The atlas of food. A space of representation, a place for policies, a methodology of territorial analyisis." *Conference Proceedings. Meeting Urban Food Needs*, Rome: FAO.

Dixon, Jane, and Cathy Banwell. 2015. "The Supermarketisation of Societies." In *Handbook of Rural Studies*, eds. M. Schucksmith, and D. Brown. Abingdon, Oxon: Routledge, 227-239.

Dixon, Jane, Cathy Banwell, Sam-ang Seubsman, Sharon Friel, and Rob MacLennan. 2007. "Dietary Diversity in Khon Kaen, 1988–2006." *International Journal of Epidemiology* 36: 518–521.

Dixon, Jane, and Emily Ballantyne-Brodie. 2015. "The Role of Planning and Design in Advancing a Bio-Nutrition Sensitive Food System." In *The Routledge Handbook of Planning for Health and Well-being*, eds. H. Barton, S. Thompson, S. Burgess, and M. Grant. Abingdon, Oxon: Routledge, 178–194.

Endo, Gen. 2013. *Diversifying Retail Distribution in Thailand*. Chiang Mai: Silkworm Books.

Endo, Gen. 2014. "The Key Role of Intermediaries in Thailand's Fresh Food Distribution System." *The International Review of Retail, Distribution and Consumer Research* 24 (5): 544–563.

Gomez, Miguel, and Katie Ricketts. 2013. "Food Value Chain Transformations in Developing Countries: Selected Hypotheses on Nutritional Implications." *Food Policy* 42:1 29–138.

Goodwin, David. 2003. "The Quality 'Turn' and Alternative Food Practices: Reflections and Agenda." *Journal of Rural Studies* 19 (1): 1–7.

Hawkes, Corinna. 2008. "Dietary Implications of Supermarket Development: A Global Perspective." *Development Policy Review* 26 (6): 657–692.

Hawkesworth, Sophie, Alan Dangour, Deborah Johnston, Karen Lock, Nigel

Poole, Jonathan Rushton, Ricardo Uauy, and Jeff Waage. 2010. "Feeding the World Healthily: The Challenge of Measuring the Effects of Agriculture on Health." *Philosophical Transactions of the Royal Society* B 365 (1554): 3083–3097.

Ingram, John S.I. 2011. "A Food Systems Approach to Researching Food Security and Its Interactions With Global Environmental Change." *Food Security* 3: 417–431.

Ingram, John, et al. 2013. "Priority Research Questions for the UK Food System." *Food Security* 5: 617–636.

Jaenicke, Hannah, and Detlef Virchow. 2013. "Entry Points Onto a Nutrition-Sensitive Agriculture." *Food Security* 5: 679–692.

Kelly, Matthew, Adrian Sleigh, Cathy Banwell, and Jane Dixon. 2010. "Nutrition Transition, Food Retailing and Health Equity in Thailand." *Australasian Epidemiologist* 13 (3): 4–7.

Kelly, Matthew, Sam-ang Seubsman, Cathy Banwell, Jane Dixon, and Adrian Sleigh. 2014. "Thailand's Food Retail Transition: Supermarket and Fresh Market Effects on Diet Quality and Health." *British Food Journal* 116 (7): 1180–1193.

Kelly, Matthew, Sam-ang Seubsman, Cathy Banwell, Jane Dixon, and Adrian Sleigh. 2015. "Traditional, Modern or Mixed? Perspectives on Social, Economic and Health Impacts of Evolving Food Retail in Thailand." *Agriculture and Human Values* 32: 445–460. doi: doi: 10.1007/s10460-014-9561-z).

McLachlan, M., and A. Landman. 2013. "Nutrition-Sensitive Agriculture – A South African Perspective." *Food Security* 5: 857–871.

Mutebi, Alex. 2007. "Regulatory Responses to Large-Format Transnational Retail in South-East Asia." *Urban Studies* 44 (2): 357–379.

Ng, S., and E. Dunford. 2013. "Complexities and Opportunities in Monitoring and Evaluating US and Glabal Changes by the Food Industry." *Obesity Reviews* 14 (S2): 29–41.

Ogle, Britta, Pham Hung, and Ho Thi Tuyet. 2001. "Significance of Wild Vegetables in Micronutrient Intakes of Women in Vietnam: An Analysis of Food Variety." *Asian Pacific Journal of Clinical Nutrition* 10 (1): 21–30.

Popkin, Barry. 2014. "Nutrition, Agriculture and the Global Food System in Low and Middle Income Countries." *Food Policy* 47 (91): 96.

Popkin, Barry, Sue Horton, and Soown Kim. 2001. "The Nutrition Transition and diet-related diseases in Asia." IFPRI Discussion Paper No. 105.

Qaim, Matin, Christine Andersson, Camilla Chege, S Kimenju, Simon Klasen, and Ramona Rischke. 2014. "Nutrition Effects of the Supermarket Revolution on Urban Consumers and Smallholder Farmers in Kenya." In *AAEA Annual Meetings* 27–29, Minneapolis, MN.

Reardon, Thomas. 2011. "The Global Rise and Impact of Supermarkets." In

Proceedings of the Crawford Fund 17th Annual Parliamentary Conference, Canberra, Australia, 14–16 August.

Reardon, Thomas, David Tschirley, Michael Dolislager, Jason Snyder, Chaoran Hu, and Stephanie White. 2014. "Urbanization, Diet Change, and Transformation of Food Supply Chains in Asia." In *Michigan State University Conference*, East Lansing, MI.

Reardon, Thomas, Peter Timmer, and Bart Minten. 2012. "Supermarket Revolution in Asia and Emerging Development Strategies to Include Small Farmers." *Proceedings of the National Academy of Sciences of the United States of America* 109 (31): 12332–12337.

Renting, H., T. Marsden, and J. Banks. 2003. "Understanding Alternative Food Networks: Exploring the Role of Short Food Supply Chains in Rural Development." *Environment and Planning A* 35: 393–411.

Ruel, Marie. 2003. "Operationalizing Dietary Diversity: A Review of Measurement Issues and Research Priorities." *American Society for Nutritional Science* 133 (11): 3911–3926.

Schipmann, Christine, and Matin Qaim. 2010. "Spillovers from Modern Supply Chains to Traditional Markets: Product Innovation and Adoption by Smallholders." *Agricultural Economics* 41 (3/4): 361–371.

Schipmann, Christine, and Matin Qaim. 2011. "Modern Food Retailers and Traditional Markets in Developing Countries: Comparing Quality, Prices and Competition Strategies in Thailand." *Applied Economic Perspectives and Policy* 33 (3): 345–362.

Shannon, Randall. 2009. "The Transformation of Food iRetailing in Thailand 1997–2007." *Asia Pacific Business Review* 15 (1): 79–92.

Sleigh, Adrian, Sam-ang Seubsman, Chris Bain, and The Thai Cohort Study Team. 2007. "Cohort Profile: The Thai Cohort of 87 134 Open University Students." *International Journal of Epidemiology* 37: 266–272.

Sriangura, V., and A. Sakseree. 2009. "Tradition Strikes Back." *Bangkok Post*, May 1.

Sriboonchitta, S., and A. Wiboonpoongse. 2008. "Overview of Contract Farming in Thailand: Lessons Learned." Tokoyo: Asian Development Bank Institute.

Stuckler, David, and Marion Nestle. 2012. "Big Food, Food Systems, and Global Health." *PLOS Medicine* 9 (6): e1001242.

Tessier, Sophie, Pierre Traissac, Bernard Maire, Nicolas Bricas, Sabrina Eymard-Duvernay, Jalila El Ati, and Francis Delpeuch. 2008. "Regular Users of Supermarkets in Greater Tunis Have a Slight Improved Diet Quality." *Journal of Nutrition* 138: 768–774.

Timmer, Peter. 2009. "Supermarkets, Modern Supply Chains, and The Changing Food Policy Agenda." Working Paper No. 162, Centre for Global Development.

Tokrisna, R. 2007. "Thailand's Changing Retail Food Sector: Consequences for Consumers, Producers, and Trade." In *PECC—Pacific Food System Outlook Meeting*, Kunming, China.

Tontisirin, K., V. Chavasit, T. Parinyasiri, M. Ditmetharoj, J. Photi, P. Intaraluk, and S. Kittiprapas. 2013. "Nutrition Impact of Agriculture and Food Systems Thailand." Edited by UN System Standing Committee on Nutrition Country Study for the Second International Conference on Nutrition.

Umberger, W., Xiaobo He, Nicolas Minot, and Hery Toiba. 2014. "Examining the Relationship Between the Use of Supermarkets and Over-Nutrition in Indonesia." In *AAEA Annual Meetings*, Mineapolis.

USDA. 2000. "Thailand Retail Food Sector 2000". GAIN Report #TH0116.

Walquist, Mark, Che Sam Lo, and Kenneth Myers. 1989. "Food Variety is Associated with Less Macrovascular Disease in Those with Type II Diabetes and Their Healthy Controls." *Journal of the American College of Nutrition* 8 (6): 515–523.

Walquist, Mark, John McKay, Ya-Chen Chang, and Ya-Wen Chiu. 2012. "Rethinking the Food Security Debate in Asia: Some Missing Ecological and Health Dimensions and Solutions." *Food Security* 4: 657–670.

Wertheim-Heck, Sigrid, Sietze Vellema, and Gert Spaargaren. 2015. "Food Safety and Urban Food Markets in Vietnam: The Need for Flexible and Customized Retail Modernization Policies." *Food Policy* 54: 95–106. doi: http://dx.doi.org/10.1016/j.foodpol.2015.05.002.

WHO. 2014. "The Top 10 Causes of Death; Fact Sheet N310." WHO. http://www.who.int/mediacentre/factsheets/fs310/en/.

Winson, Anthony. 2013. *The Industrial Diet. The Degradation of Food and The Struggle for Healthy Eating.* Vancouver: UBC Press.

Wiskerke, J. 2009. "On Places Lost and Places Regained: Reflections on the Alternative Food Geography and Sustainable Regional Development." *International Planning Studies* 14 (4): 369-387.

Yasmeen, G. 2000. "Not 'From Scratch': Thai Food Systems and 'Public Eating.'" *Journal of Intercultural Studies* 21 (3): 341–352.

Table 1: Associations of food shopping patterns with health and diet outcomes among 1349 Thai Cohort Study sub-sample

	Shopping pattern*		
	Fresh market shoppers (N=720) proportion	Mixed shoppers (N=255) proportion	Supermarket shoppers (N=373) proportion
Consumption at least weekly:			
Fast foods	**6.5**	**9.1**	**12.8**
Soft drinks	**25**	**32**	**30**
Instant foods	**19**	**19.3**	**24.2**
Deep fried foods	**73.4**	**74.1**	**75.6**
Overweight or obese	48.6	49.5	49.7
High cholesterol	**38.7**	**40.5**	**47.8**
Ischemic heart disease	**1.9**	**1.7**	**4.3**
Sufficient fruit consumption**	**73.8**	**70**	**66.7**
Sufficient vegetable consumption**	**74.9**	**73.3**	**69.4**
Combined fruit and vegetable consumption sufficient**	**57.6**	**52.1**	**48.1**
	Mean change (kg)		
Mean weight change 2012–2013	0.28	0.44	0.5

Figures in bold indicate that column proportions were significantly different with p<0.05, that is, there were significant differences between shopping pattern groups for that indicator.

* Shopping pattern of individuals in 2012 was based on reported frequency of shopping at various food retail formats. Those who shopped more at traditional fresh markets were placed in the first category, more regular supermarket shoppers in the supermarket category, and those who shopped equally in each format were categorized as "mixed shoppers."
** Using Thai Recommended Daily servings of three serves of vegetables and two serves of fruit per day.

Toward a Restricted Tolerance of Street Vending of Food in Hanoi Districts: The Role of Stakeholder Dialogue

Nguyen Thi Tan Loc[A] & Paule Moustier[B]

In Vietnam, fruit and vegetable marketing is characterized by a diversity of distribution chains, including formal markets, street vendors, shops, and supermarkets. The government is promoting the expansion of supermarket distribution and plans to eliminate all informal trade on the grounds of modernization. The article investigates how the activities of street vendors can be successfully integrated in the city, using a stakeholder dialogue approach. Researchers appraised the role of street vendors in food distribution and employment and documented a successful street vending model. Stakeholder meetings were held to discuss the integration of street vending in Dong Da District. A key result is the demonstration and recognition by city and district officials of the dominant role of street vending in food distribution and employment of the poor. Workshops helped the Hanoi city and district authorities agree to tolerate street vendors in selected areas, with the setting of jointly developed commitments.

Keywords: *Street vendors, Vietnam, food distribution, stakeholder dialogue, informal markets*

Introduction

During the past 20 years, the food sector in Vietnam has undergone major changes. The reforms implemented in the framework of the *doi moi*, or "renovation" policy, have been reflected in spectacular economic growth, particularly in cities. In 2013, the growth rate of the economy was 5%, the urbanization growth rate 3%, and the urbanization rate 33%, contrasting with 25% in 2002. Economic and demographic changes have caused an increase in the demand for more diverse and better quality produce, especially in urban areas. The food distribution sector has adapted to these changes and has now taken on a diversity of forms. In Hanoi, a person can purchase foodstuffs from a variety of sources ranging from street vendors to air-conditioned hypermarkets, with shops and fixed market stalls in between (Figuié and Moustier 2009; Mergenthaler,

[A] Fruit and Vegetable Research Institute, Trau Quy, Hanoi, Vietnam.

[B] Centre de Coopération Internationale en Recherche Agronomique pour le Développement (CIRAD), UMR MOISA, France.

doi: 10.18278/wfp.2.2.3.1.5

Weinberger, and Qaim 2009). Yet, this diversity is currently threatened by the government's clear promotion of modern high-volume distribution and the planned eradication of informal trade activities, including that of street vendors. In the Vietnam context, we define street vendors as persons selling from baskets, motorbikes, or bicycles, usually moving from one place to the other, sometimes forming groups to sell on stretches of pavement or in other vacant spaces. This is in line with the definition given by Bhowmik (2005). The planned fast-track increase of supermarkets and elimination of temporary markets and street vendors is indicated in the strategy put forward by the Domestic Trade Department of the Ministry of Trade from the present until 2020, on the grounds of "modernizing" and "civilizing" commerce (Vietnam Ministry of Trade 2006). Regulation 36CP on traffic order and safety (dated February 2003) made street vending illegal, mostly because of traffic issues. However, in January 2009, street vending was actually recognized by Decision 46/2009 of the Hanoi People Committee, but prohibited on 63 major streets and some 48 public spaces including hospitals, squares, and bus stations.

At the same time, although Vietnam is praised for its success in poverty alleviation, poverty and unemployment are still major concerns for the government and donors. Poverty in Vietnam is mostly rural. In 2010, the average poverty rate was 20%, while the urban poverty rate was between 6% and 7%. Yet, urban poverty is underestimated as most migrants are not registered and do not benefit from social services. And the percentage of urban residents who suffer from non-monetary deprivations is much higher than the poverty rate (World Bank 2012; Thanh, Anh, and Phuong 2013).

Food distribution by itinerant vendors is well known to be a key factor in the social inclusion of the poor, as it creates small-scale business activities and has a positive impact in giving the poor access to food commodities. In Asia, their numbers have kept increasing in the last 10 years because of growing unemployment problems in cities, where in most of them it is estimated that informal jobs outnumber formal jobs (Bhowmik, op. cit.).

Making street vending an illegal activity and therefore making those who are engaged in it subject to a number of threats is not specific to Vietnam, as many countries in Asia and Africa have declared street vending illegal. The banning of street vending usually results from alleged traffic or health issues, often linked to modernization projects that favor large-scale and capital-intensive investments (Cross 2000). Asian governments typically have a policy of increasing formal employment and eliminating informal employment. A more pragmatic approach is to allow "semi-formality," in other words promote a self-regulating system with regulatory enforcement reduced to a minimum, thus protecting the flexibility of street vending which is uniquely adapted to the conditions of the urban poor (Cross, op. cit.).

The experience of other countries shows cases of successful integration of street vending in urban planning when street vendors are organized and dialogue is maintained with authorities.

The organization of street vendors into advocacy groups is documented as the first step toward legalization, albeit partial.

Success stories of integration of street vendors in Kenya (Mitullah 2003) or India (Mahadevia et al. 2013) are in line with a stakeholder approach, which puts the economic agents who are affected by the policy decisions and actions of the system at the core of the decision processes (Grimble et al. 1995). The first objective of the article is to highlight the economic and social importance of fruit and vegetable street vending in Hanoi. The second objective is to show how stakeholder dialogue, based on such an evaluation and organized interactions between street vendors, urban authorities, consumers, and researchers, enables a more harmonious integration of food vending in the urban frame.

Method

The method is based on the stakeholder approach in which we consider street vendors as entrepreneurs with objectives and constraints that are influenced by other stakeholders with whom they interact. It is noteworthy that while stakeholder dialogue based on scientific knowledge has been widely used in the field of natural resource management (Reed, 2008, Grimble et al. 1995), its application to food marketing issues is not frequent, which highlights the originality of the research paper. We consider it to be particularly relevant in a context of diverging interests and diverse perceptions that characterize the food street vending sector in Vietnam. Some

stakeholders are particularly influential on street vendors' activities: their customers, police agents, as well as district and city officials from the department of trade. We assumed that their perception of street vendors may be influenced: (i) by the scientific knowledge that we could provide as international and local researchers on their social and economic role; (ii) by the way the street vendors express their objectives and constraints; (iii) and by the dialogue fostered among street vendors, police agents, district, and city officials, as well as local customers, on ways to reconcile diverging objectives. This perception influences their attitudes and actions toward street vending (see Figure 1). Hence, in this research, the article authors (termed as "we") acted at the same time as researchers and facilitators.

We made various studies of the street vendor activity in Hanoi to appraise their social and economic role. The first one was done in 2004 and updated in 2009 and 2013. We estimated the number of vegetable and fruit street vendors in Hanoi and the volume of goods sold by them. In 2009 and 2014, we also estimated the number and volumes traded by other points of sale to estimate the contribution of street vending to total food distribution. We interviewed a sample of street vendors to appraise the role of street vending in their livelihood and the impact of the legislation on their activities. This involved 60 street vendors in 2004 and 160 in 2013. A discussion paper was prepared based on the information generated, which provided the basis for a stakeholder workshop held in 2006, chaired by the Hanoi Department and Trade with the participation of a

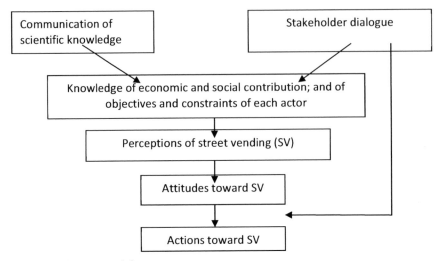

Figure 1: Conceptual frame

panel of street vendors, consumers, the heads of departments, and technical divisions dealing with agriculture and trade and included persons from market management boards, public security, the Department of Health, the Women's Union, the People's Committee of six different districts, as well as a panel of street vendors, along with the researchers involved in the study. In addition, in 2013, we documented one successful street vending model, in Kim Lien Ward in Dong Da District, by interviewing 16 consumers and 14 street vendors at this market.

On the basis of the gathered information, we organized a stakeholder dialogue process at the district level. In 2013, after interchange with the Hanoi Department of Industry and Trade, we organized three meetings bringing together street vendors and the competent authorities, including the Hanoi Department of Industry and Trade, district and ward officials, residential group representatives, and consumers in three wards of Dong Da District (Phuong Mai, Trung Tu, and Lang Ha). The meetings took place on March 8, March 14, and March 19, respectively. The objective was to discuss the results and to replicate the support from the authorities who helped unofficial sellers by giving them the permission to sell produce on vacant pieces of land and along dead-end streets. We found the street vendors themselves require support in the form of raising their awareness of environmental sanitation, traffic safety, food hygiene, and food safety. We held three training courses for street vendors in these wards, with the participation of local officials. The changes in street vendors' behavior were assessed in these wards, which helped the local authorities see that they had grounds to continue their support for street vending activities.

In this article, we highlight the updated data on the economic contribution made by street vendors. We also present the results achieved by the stakeholder dialogue in Dong Da District and discuss the benefits of applying a stakeholder approach to the issue of street vending in Hanoi. This makes the article complementary to our previously published work on street vending in Hanoi (Moustier et al. 2007; 2009; Nguyen Thi Tan Loc et al. 2013).

Selected results

We first present the results of our studies aimed at quantifying the economic and social role of fruit and vegetables street vending in Hanoi. Then we describe the successful experience in Kim Lien involving a street vendors' temporary market. This evidence served as the basis for stakeholder dialogue in Dong Da District, which will be presented at the end of this section.

The importance of street vending in urban food distribution

Consumer's surveys have shown that poor residents of Hanoi purchase produce mainly from street vendors due to its low price, freshness, and proximity to their homes (Figuié and Moustier 2009). Street vendors source vegetables mostly from wholesale markets (in urban areas) and partly from their own production. In 2009, vegetable street vendors supplied 32% of the total vegetable volume sold

to consumers, compared to 58% for retail markets, 9% for shops, and 1% for supermarkets. Until 2009, the number of vegetable street vendors increased at a higher rate than that of the city's population.

In 2014, we estimated that ~45% of vegetables were sold by street vendors, 49% at retail markets, with a limited volume being sold at stores (3%) and supermarkets (3%). This suggests an increase in the number of vendors and the volume they sell. We explain it by the movement of vendors from official markets to unofficial markets, especially along the road sides near factories, schools, or in front of someone's house or a store to avoid having to pay increasingly high fees in renovated official markets.

The importance of street vending for the livelihoods of the poor

The importance of street vendors in terms of poverty alleviation is both to the ones they serve and to the vendors themselves. Street vending not only contributes to delivering fruits and vegetables to low- and medium-income consumers, but also improves the livelihood of urban and peri-urban residents with limited income opportunities. Street vendors are mostly female residents of Hanoi or neighboring provinces. They may once have been involved in agriculture, but their fields have been reduced in size due to urban development. They may still be able to grow some vegetables or buy vegetables from neighbors to sell in order to supplement their family income. With low qualifications, street vendors have limited options for employment although they are the main income-generating workers of their family. These street vendors consider street vending as a family profession. As a result, even though street vendors face daily risks and must work hard, they have to continue their street vending activity because they need the income it brings. However, street vending is not a stable occupation: it depends on external factors which cause many difficulties for the vendors.

Threats to the business of street vendors

Overall, two thirds of the street vendors interviewed had been arrested and fined at least once a month. This can happen on any street, whether street vending is prohibited on it or not. When street vending is not prohibited, they may be arrested for allegedly hindering traffic. The amount of the fine is about twice

their daily profit. Yet, street vendors, especially the older ones, develop a range of strategies to avoid paying the fines, including playing on the "emotional guilt" of police officers and finding the weak spots in police surveillance (Turner and Schoenberger 2011).

An example of successful integration of street vending in the city

Recently, the authorities in some wards made efforts to help unofficial sellers to set up temporarily on vacant land or along low-traffic dead-end streets. The sellers manage such places by themselves and do not have to pay any fees. After each morning session of market selling, the vendors clean up the entire market space, which is then used as a playground in the afternoon (see Box 1).

Box 1. The example of Kim Lien market

> The Kim Lien market is a model of successfully integrating street vending in the city. It sprung from the initiative of local residents, street vendors, and ward authorities in 2004 after a number of street vendors had been expelled from a street slated for widening. Initially, 20 street vendors began selling produce in this market, but the number has increased to the 70 currently. Street vendors are aware that the local leaders have made it possible for them to sell at the market. In acknowledgement, they feel responsible for keeping the area very clean.
>
> The customers are mainly residents of Kim Lien ward, while a few come from elsewhere. The proportion of elderly or retired people in this ward is quite high and they choose to buy products in this temporary market because they do not have to travel far. Hence, they are supportive of the street vendors.
>
> Phuong Mai ward has a street where informal marketing takes place along the lines of the Kim Lien market, thanks to the involvement of the head of a residential group.

The results of stakeholder dialogue

We first present the rationale of stakeholder dialogue in Hanoi to contribute solving the problems related to street vendors. As explained in the introduction, the perceptions and attitudes of the district and city officials relative to informal food trade were initially negative and interventions were top-down. Our conversations with the officials and analysis of official documents (Hanoi Department of Trade 2010; Vietnam Ministry of Trade 2006) show that the informal food trade was considered as a leftover of backward activities, with a negative impact on traffic and food safety, and which should be made to disappear quickly and be replaced by supermarkets and markets equipped with cold storage and concrete buildings. The result was that facilities were provided to supermarket investors in terms of access to land, and building four "modern" retail markets on sites where the older markets previously stood (Geertman 2011; Hanoi Department of Trade 2010). It also resulted into the continuous harassment of street vendors by the police. But this top-down approach has many limitations. The fees to get access to market stalls are so prohibitively high that the number of street vendors decreased somewhat between 2009 and 2013 and has actually increased since (Nguyen Thi Tan Loc et al., 2013). At the same time, many consumers, especially the less well-to-do, prefer to get their supplies from vendors close to them, at low prices, rather than from distant supermarkets and markets which require fees for parking and where food is usually more expensive than that sold by street vendors.

Box 2. Some quotes by residents and street vendors

Mrs N.T.T., a resident of Phuong Mai ward stated: "Areas where street vendors commonly sell products are in essence small markets. They are a feature wherever low-income consumers live. Street vendors sell produce at price levels that suit them. However, we are concerned about the quality of vegetables sold. Therefore, we hope that the ward authority will arrange frequent spot checks on the quality of vegetables."

"I have been retired since 1986. To ensure my family's daily subsistence, the only income-generating activity I can do is vegetables street vending," said Mrs NTD in Quang Trung Ward. She adds: "I often purchase vegetables at the Phung Khoang wholesale market because they are mainly from safe vegetable growing areas in Dong Anh District." She concludes by expressing the wish that "the ward will arrange a stable area for street vendors."

Consumers found it important to have makeshift selling points to meet the demand of the local residents, especially elderly persons who have restricted mobility and financial capacity. Consumers highlighted the advantages of these points: low prices, freshness, and friendly relationships between sellers and consumers. However, they are concerned about produce origin (in particular, they prefer vegetables that originate from periurban areas where production conditions have been certified as "safe" by Hanoi authorities) and accurate weighing by street vendors. If these concerns were addressed, street vending would be fully supported by the residents (see Box 2).

The street vendors pointed out that their activity generated employment and income for themselves and their families. There is no other activity that they can engage in. Hence, street vending contributes to employment, family stability, and social security. Street vendors, often farmers themselves, say that they pay attention to the way the vegetables are produced and make purchases of vegetables based on their origin (see Box 2).

As for the difficulties faced by street vendors from the police, the police representatives replied that street vendors frequently disrupt traffic by crossing streets just anywhere or setting up on places that obstruct traffic.

The main objectives and constraints of stakeholders are summarized in Table 1.

Based on the experience in Kim Lien market and Phuong Mai Ward, participants reached a consensus on what makes a good street vending model. First, there must be a meeting of minds among the residential group leaders. A representative of the residential group is needed who is willing to take some risk and build a relationship with the Communist Party secretaries of the residential groups and local Women's Union. This ensures the support of the ward leaders. Second, there must be cooperation on the part of ward leaders who understand the street vendors need to earn a living. In all cases, there

Table 1. Main objectives and constraints of stakeholders

	Street vendors	**Residents**	**Policemen**
Objectives	Livelihoods	Cheap access to food Trust in food safety	Fluid traffic
Constraints	High fines	Little knowledge on origin of food	Torn between compassion and duty

must also be good cooperation with the residential groups where street vendors operate. Crucially, in order to maintain this model in the long term, a consensus among the ward, district, and city leaders is needed. This is only possible when street vending is allowed in specific areas, such as on plots of vacant land, unoccupied yards, stretches of pavement, or the like, and is under good management, keeping its impact on traffic, the environment, and urban landscape to a strict minimum. The cooperation, involvement, and support of the city, district, and ward leaders is crucial in order to set up local marketplaces for street vendors.

A valuable point noted by the research team is that the stakeholders across the board must share in the effort.

- People living around the marketplace need to accept a bit of noise and loss of space where street vendors set up on both sides of the street.
- Street vendors must maintain order, discipline, tidiness, and cleanliness.
- Garbage collection workers should cooperate to help clear up waste after each market session, sharing the work with the street vendors.

The leaders of residential groups must be responsible for seeing that street vendors sit at their designated places and that cleanup is done after the market session. They must also look into the quality of the produce sold and remind street vendors of their obligations as needed.

Ward, district, and city leaders expressed their interest in working toward this model. Moreover, the street vendors participating to workshops said that they would like to raise awareness among other street vendors about the need to comply with street vending regulations. They also specifically asked for support to overcome problems with food safety. They want other vendors to be well-informed in order to reduce risks, deal with hygiene issues, identify unsafe vegetable and fruit produce, as well as risks in the process of produce selection and sales. There was a consensus on the necessity to sustain the successful cases of integration of street vending in the wards, e.g., Kim Liem market, and to replicate this experience in other areas.

Conclusions

The research we presented demonstrates how a stakeholder approach can help to overcome the hostility that authorities and consumers may feel toward street vendors. This means providing a better understanding of the objectives and constraints on both sides. The literature review shows that rather than trying to convert informal activities into formal activities, a more pragmatic approach is to upgrade them in the context of developing economies (Bhowmik, op. cit.).

The research on fruit and vegetable street vending enabled the research team to demonstrate the significant contribution of this activity to the livelihoods of the poor and to food distribution. From the standpoint of the authorities and consumers, street vending activities bring advantages but admittedly may be a cause of traffic obstruction and give rise to consumer concerns over food safety.

The main outcomes of the research and consultation are that management staff at the ward and district levels as well as within the Department of Industry and Trade now have a fuller understanding of street vending and see the importance for leaders to facilitate things to allow street vendors to operate in residential areas. This approach was original in that local residents—the customers of the street vendors—were involved in the consultation. The example of the Kim Lien market and street vending in Phuong Mai Ward shows that groups of customers can take a sustained interest in promoting the activities of street vendors, in tandem with the local authorities who give permission for vacant land to be used. Street vendors themselves commit to following traffic and food safety regulations. In this way, the street vending becomes "semi-formal," so to speak, which means that the system of stakeholders is self-regulating. Regulations are enforced while flexibly and entry barriers to trading activities can be kept low for the benefit of less affluent urban residents (Cross op. cit.). Some elements in our work on promoting stakeholder recognition and dialogue for a better integration of informal activities in a city can be replicated, even though the political context is quite specific. In Hanoi, it is particularly difficult to foster collective action by street vendors because of the attitude of local authorities who consider that any form of organization should come from their initiative and operate under their control. So we had to invite a panel of street vendors representing a diversity of socio-economic profiles and have them agree to disseminate information to their acquaintances rather than acting as actual representatives of the vendors. Further, support was sought from the Women's Union at the city and local levels, given its rather direct interest in this issue. The general lessons can be summarized as follows: first, this action-research shows the importance of gathering rigorous qualitative and quantitative data on the benefits and drawbacks of the informal activity under focus. Researchers are also particularly helpful in documenting success stories of the inclusion of informal activities in the city, internationally, and locally. Second, it suggests that confining the scale to the ward or district may make it easier to implement fruitful stakeholder dialogue than taking on the scale of the city. This more localized scale is also relevant to identify and document innovative solutions to the problems posed by street vending. Third, having informal traders, consumers, district and ward officers as well as researchers involved in the dialogue process led by skilled facilitators, getting all to express their views on the issue at stake, reaching a measure of consensus and making commitments on solutions to the problems raised, are important ingredients for success. As a follow-up, it would be necessary to regularly monitor the process put in place and facilitate further stakeholder dialogue. From a research perspective, investigating recent insights from policy and planning sciences, including Public Participation, would also be very valuable (Innes and Booher 2004; Walker, McQuarrie, and Lee 2015).

Acknowledgments

The research was first carried out between 2008 and 2010 in the framework of a collaboration between "Markets for the Poor," a project funded by the ADB and DFID, and MALICA, a research consortium on food markets in Asia which includes CIRAD, VAAS, and IPSARD. In 2013, DFID, through the Sustainable Markets program of IIED, funded an updated documentation of the role of street vending in Hanoi and new stakeholder consultations. This resulted in a publication of an IIED paper in 2013. Finally, some new market surveys were conducted in 2014 in the context of Nguyen Thi Tan Loc's Ph.D. thesis, with financial support from CIRAD.

References

Bhowmik, S.K. 2005. "Street Vendors in Asia: A Review." *Economic and Political Weekly*, 2256-2264.

Cross, J. 2000. "Street Vendors, and Postmodernity: Conflict and Compromise in the Global Economy." *International Journal of Sociology and Social Policy* 20 (1/2): 29-51.

Figuié, M., and P. Moustier. 2009. "Market Appeal in An Emerging Economy: Supermarkets and Poor Consumers in Vietnam." *Food Policy* 34 (2): 210-217.

Geertman, S. 2011. "Fresh Markets, a Way of Life and Public Health Under Threat. Experiences in Europe and Asia and Action for Hanoi." Consultancy Report. Hanoi: Healthbridge.

Grimble, R., M.K. Chan, J. Agliontsy, and J. Quan. 1995. *Trees and Trade-Offs: A Stakeholder Approach to Natural Resource Management*. London: IIED.

Hanoi Department of Trade. 2010. "Overview of Current Status and Direction of Economic and Social Development in Hanoi in 2010, and 2030 Vision."

Thanh, H-X., T. T. Anh, and D. T. T. Phuong. 2013. "Urban Poverty in Vietnam: A View from Complementary Assessments." IIED Human Settlements Working Paper Series, n°40. London: IIED.

Innes, J.E., and D.E. Booher. 2004. "Reframing Public Participation: Strategies for the 21st Century." *Planning Theory and Practice* 5: 419-436.

Mahadevia, D., A. Brown, M. Lyons, S. Vyas, K. Jajoo, and A. Mishra. 2013. Street Vendors in Ahmedabad: Status, Contribution and Challenges Report: Working Paper 20, Centre for Urban Equity. Ahmedabad: CEPT University.

Mergenthaler, M., K. Weinberger, and M. Qaim. 2009. "Consumer Valuation of Food Quality and Food Safety Attributes in Vietnam." *Applied Economic Perspectives and Policy* 31 (2): 266-283.

Mitullah, W. 2003. "Street Trade in Kenya: The Contribution of Research in Policy Dialogue and Response." *Urban Research Symposium on Urban Development for Economic Growth and Poverty Reduction*, Washington, World Bank, December 2003, 15-17.

Moustier, P., M. Figuié, T.A. Dao, and T.T.L. Nguyen. 2009. "Are Supermarkets Poor-Friendly? Debates and Evidence from Vietnam." In *The Crisis of Food Brands*, eds. Lindgreen A., and Hingley M. London, New York, Gower and Routledge, 311-327.

Moustier, P., Nguyen Thi Tan Loc, Ho Thanh Son, and Hoang Bang An. 2007. "Promotion of Public-Private Dialogue to Maintain Poor-friendly Fruit and Vegetable Street Vending in Hanoi." *Acta Horticulturae* 794: 239-247.

Nguyen, Thi Tan Loc, Paule Moustier, Le Nhu Thinh, and Le Thi Ha. 2013. "Inclusive Urban Development? Making Space for Street Vending in Hanoi, Vietnam." London: IIED.

Reed, M.S. 2008. "Stakeholder Participation for Environmental Management: A Literature Review." *Biological conservation* 141 (10): 2417-2431.

Vietnam Ministry of Trade, Department of Domestic Market Policies. 2006. The Strategy for Domestic Trade Development for the Period 2010–2015 and Development Orientation to 2020. Hanoi: Ministry of Trade, 30.

Turner, S., and L. Schoenberger. 2011. "Street Vendor Livelihoods and Everyday Politics in Hanoi, Vietnam: The Seeds of a Diverse Economy?" *Urban Studies*, 49 (5), 1027-1044.

Walker, E.T., M. McQuarrie, and C.W. Lee. 2015. "Rising Participation and Declining Democracy." In *Democratizing Inequalities: Dilemmas of the New Public Participation*, eds C W. Lee, M. McQuarrie, E. T. Walker. New York: New York University Press, 3-22.

World Bank. 2012. "Well Begun, Not Yet Done: Vietnam's Remarkable Progress on Poverty Reduction and the Emerging Challenges." Report. Hanoi: World Bank.

Constructing a Database for Food Security Assessments in Southeast Asia

Ulrike Grote[A] & Hermann Waibel[A]

In many Southeast Asian countries, food insecurity remains an important problem. However, the assessment of food security is often difficult due to the lack of adequate data. Studies undertaken by international organizations are mostly rapid appraisal type of analyses lacking scientific rigor and depth. Against this background there is a need to establish sound databases, which allow for more in-depth analyses. Although the collection of data in remote rural areas of poor countries is challenging, data quality is crucial in order to advance research on the economics of food security. Own case studies from Southeast Asia highlight the need to account for multidimensional facets of food security in data collection. They highlight the need to differentiate between monetary and nonmonetary poverty aspects and to look into diverse livelihood activities. They also stress the importance of the time dimension due to price increases or many other shocks and coping strategies. We suggest incorporating food security research into long-term panel data projects such as the long-term panel data project for Thailand and Vietnam, which we believe is unique and valuable also for food security assessments.

Keywords: food security, case studies, database, assessment, Southeast Asia

Introduction

In September 2015, the United Nations (UN) decided to adopt the post-2015 development agenda. It consists of 17 Sustainable Development Goals (SDGs) as a follow-up to the Millennium Development Goals which have been only partly reached. The new goals and targets aim to stimulate further action over the coming 15 years in areas of critical importance for the whole planet (UN 2015). The second of the 17 SDGs is directed toward achieving food security and improved nutrition, among others.

Food security remains a prevailing problem in many developing countries, including Southeast Asia. Assessing food insecurity is often impaired by the lack

[A] Leibniz University Hannover, Germany

doi: 10.18278/wfp.2.2.3.1.6

of adequate data. Studies undertaken by international organizations with a mandate to solve the food insecurity problem are mostly rapid appraisal type of analyses which are not always in-depth and scientifically rigorous. Because of their aim to provide quick results, these assessment measures often focus on availability and access to food, and give less emphasis on utilization of food and long-term stability. Hence, there is a need for research to better understand the determinants and drivers of food security in order to contribute to a long-term solution of the problem.

Against this background, this article promotes the notion of establishing panel databases that allow undertaking in-depth and causal analyses in food security. We map out some requirements for databases that can serve such purposes. Next to sampling issues, the choice of regions and the questionnaire design will be discussed. Also, the use of focus group discussions has been useful in deriving some further qualitative insights into food security.

This article displays the shortcomings on the use of food security concepts and measures on the one hand, and sheds some light on the determinants of food security of households on the other hand. Case studies and examples from selected Southeast Asian countries are provided.

The article is structured as follows: following the introduction, the literature on the status of food security assessments is reviewed. The dimensions of the food security concept, its measurement, and shortcomings as well as some of its determinants are introduced. The next section provides case studies from

selected Southeast Asian countries. Furthermore data requirements for food security assessment are highlighted. The last section summarizes and concludes.

Food Security Assessments: A Literature Review

Defining "food security"

The concept of food security includes manifold definitions most of which are descriptive. Maxwell and Frankenberger (1992) have identified >30 definitions for "food security" and Hoddinott (1999) claims that there are ~200 definitions of food security which are used by different organizations around the world. The perhaps most accepted and most widely cited definition of food security has been phrased at the World Food Summit in 1996 as "a situation when all people, at all times, have physical, social, and economic access to sufficient, safe, and nutritious food to meet their dietary needs and food preferences for an active and healthy life" (FAO 1996). Food security has been further specified to involve four dimensions consisting of food availability, access, utilization, and the stability of these conditions (WFP 2009a).

Food availability refers to the actual availability of food in physical terms. It can be either applied at the national level combining domestic production, food stocks as well as food imports and food aid, or it is measured at the regional or local level (WFP 2009a; 2009b; FAO 2006). Access of a household to food is the most critical dimension of food security; accordingly, it is the dimension being most often assessed by researchers and international organizations and most often used to describe food secure households (Maxwell, Vaitla, and Coates 2014; Coates 2013; FAO 2011; Wiesmann et al. 2009). Economic access reflects a household's ability to acquire food in sufficient quantity and quality and can be realized based on own production, market purchases, remittances, or barter trade. Social access, however, might be limited due to discrimination of gender or minorities (WFP 2009a; 2008b; FAO 2006). This means that even though enough food might be available, some households might not be able to access it. The utilization of food refers to the quality and safety of food or its nutrients content. It includes behavioral, health, and hygiene aspects (Carletto, Zezza, and Banerjee 2013; FAO 2006). Stability covers dynamic aspects such as seasonal fluctuations, shocks, and long-term developments. In this regard a distinction is made between chronic and transitory food insecurity (Devereux 2006; Maxwell and Smith 1992). In consequence, the stability dimension of food security is similar to the concept of vulnerability to poverty (Hart 2009); Devereux (2006) has defined vulnerability to food insecurity as "the exposure and sensitivity to livelihood shocks."

Existing concepts and measures of food security

In the last 20 years, numerous measures, especially for food access, have been developed (Coates 2013). We summarize these concepts and their related food security indicators in Table 1, categorizing them into process and outcome indicators following Maxwell and Frankenberger (1992). Process indicators for food availability refer to measures for agricultural production, access to natural resources, institutional development, or market infrastructure, while those for food access relate to the means and strategies of households to achieve food security, such as migration, sale of assets, or collection of wild foods.

Outcome indicators include the household calorie intake which is generally derived from consumption recall surveys over a predetermined period of time and measures the amount of energy consumed over a defined reference period. i.e., a day or week (Hoddinott 1999; Jones et al. 2013). The food consumption score (FCS) relates to food access but it considers a qualitative and a quantitative dimension. It is calculated based on how frequently a household consumed different food groups during the last 7 days. It has been developed based on the fact that it is difficult to collect very detailed data on food or calorie intake. The FCS thus approximates food consumption considering the diversity of diets, the frequency of food intake, and the relative nutritional importance of food groups (WFP 2008a). The diversity of diets relates to the number of food groups a household has consumed during the week. Food frequency considers the number of days the household has consumed certain food groups, and the nutritional importance depends on the nutrients in terms of calories, macro-, and micronutrients. The food groups cover (i) main staples, (ii) pulses, (iii) vegetables, (iv) fruits, (v) meat and fish, (vi) milk, (vii) sugar, and (viii) oil, and they are weighted and then summed up into an aggregate score. The food groups with high energy content, good quality protein, and micronutrients receive the highest weight of 4, and sugar and oil the lowest of 0.5. Households with a FCS <35 are then classified as food insecure. A score of 21 was indicated to be the minimum.

The household diet diversity score (HDDS) is also derived from consumption recall surveys, but preferably for a 24 hours recall period (Hoddinott 1999; Jones et al. 2013; Jones, Shrinivas, and Bezner-Kerr 2014). It is an indicator for dietary quality and captures how many food items or food groups a household has consumed. It distinguishes between 11 food groups and simply sums the number of different food groups. Accordingly, the HDDS ranges between 0 and 11 for households with the most diverse diet. Thresholds dividing households into high- or low-diversity groups are not provided.

Finally, the household food insecurity access scale (HFIAS) (Swindale and Bilinski 2006) is a survey-based-outcome indicator where respondents answer a set of nine questions that give a subjective measure of a household's food insecurity status. These include domains like anxiety/uncertainty about food access, quality of food, and quantity of food. The set of questions identified for each domain represents the experience of food insecurity (access) under that domain. The questions are meant to be universally understandable and in principle can be adapted to different cultural contexts provided consistency of the concept is maintained.

Anthropometric measures are usually applied as a proxy of food utilization and reflect chronic or acute mal- or undernourishment (Jones et al. 2013). The most frequently used measures are weight for age (WFA) and height for age (HFA), both referred to children with age <5 years. If the weight of a child is too low for the height, the term "wasting" is used. Stunted children are too short for their age, indicating mal- and undernutrition (de Haen et al. 2011). Child underweight combines the two indicators and is defined as a low weight for age ratio.

To sum up, the choice of indicators for assessing the food security status is crucial. Different indicators often come to very different assessments for the same food security situation (de Haen et al. 2011). Development organizations such as FAO often suggest that food security assessments should include several indicators in order to capture the multidimensional facets of food security. There is currently no consensus which indicators should be given priority to and to what extent they are complements or substitutes (see, e.g., Maxwell, Vaitla, and Coates 2014; Headey and Ecker 2013; Coates 2013; Jones et al. 2013; Carletto, Zezza, and Banerjee 2013).

Headey and Ecker (2013) stressed that the accurate measurement of food security at micro or macro levels is of vital importance as policymakers and NGOs respond to it. Carletto, Zezza, and Banerjee (2013) noted that a consensus on appropriate indicators would benefit the measurement of global food security and the coordination between organizations. Consequently, more research is needed. Such research should not be limited to just measuring the extent of the food security problem but should focus on the causes of food insecurity.

Table 1. Overview of food security concepts and related indicators

Concept	Authors	Indicator(s)	Strength	Weakness
		Process indicators		
Availability	Maxwell and Frankenberger (1992)	Agricultural output Access to natural resources Market infrastructure	a) Readily available b) Secondary statistics	a) Weak correlation with food security b) One dimensional c) Imprecise
Access	Maxwell and Frankenberger (1992)	Migration Sale of assets Collection of wild foods	a) Evidence on links to food security b) Measurable in surveys	a) Primary surveys needed b) One-dimensional
		Outcome indicators		
Access	Jones et al. (2013)	Household calorie intake	Household recall surveys	a) Only in quantitative terms
Access	WFP (2008a)	Food consumption score (FCS)	a) Consumption surveys b) Well accepted	a) Only yes-no information
Access	Hoddinot (1999), Hoddinott and Yohannes (2002)	Household diet diversity score (HDDS)	a) Can use consumption survey data b) Correlate with measures of food consumption	a) 24 h recall surveys time consuming, b) No thresholds like in FCS
Access	Swindale and Bilinsky (2006)	Household food insecurity access scale	Can easily be incorporated in surveys	Questions may be culturally sensitive
Access and utilization	WHO (1986), Svedberg (2011)	Weight for age Height for age Weight for height	Data easily collected in livelihood surveys	a) Actual measurements are time consuming in surveys b) Do not cover nutrients which might be deficient

Source: own presentation

Drivers of household food insecurity

As emphasized in the literature, the most important determinant of a household's food security status is poverty (e.g., von Braun et al. 1992; Barrett 2010). Ahmed et al. (2009) compared poverty and food consumption across 20 countries and found a high correlation between living below the poverty line and consuming an insufficient amount of calories. The Asian Development Bank in its 2014 key indicator report (ADB 2014) has proposed the upward adjustment of the poverty line by weighting food consumption shares with the food price index. It was estimated that by doing so the number of poor people in Asia would be ~15% higher (ADB 2014).

Demographic characteristics and endowment with human capital of the household have also been found to be important determinants of food insecurity. For example, food insecure households tend to have more members in general, but also more young children and older dependents who do not contribute to the household's income (von Braun et al. 1992). Education helps households to improve their skills and productivity or engage in better paying jobs, thus having a positive effect on food security as it (WFP 2009b; Bogale 2012). The gender of the household head determines household's food security, although the results so far have been ambiguous. Kassie, Ndiritu, and Stage (2014) found that female-headed households in Kenya are more likely to be food insecure. Fuwa (2000) found that female-headed households face a "triple burden": (1) they are often the single earners, (2) they face various disadvantages in the labor or financial

market, e.g., they have limited access to credit, and (3) they are responsible for maintaining the household and childcare. On the other hand, as shown in different settings in Africa, Asia, and Latin America (Quisumbing et al. 1995; von Braun et al. 1992), female-headed households can also be more food secure due to the fact that women spent more of their income on food than men.

Other drivers of food security for rural households relate to the ownership of land and livestock, or distance. While landowners are able to grow food for own consumption and/or sale, landless households depend on other often scarce and low-paid employment opportunities and tend to be more food insecure (von Braun et al. 1992). With respect to livestock, it is an important source of protein and micronutrients, such as iron or vitamin A, if consumed at home, but at the same time if sold, it provides income and bartering power, and serves as a buffer for food insecure times (FAO 2011). Jones, Shrinivas, and Bezner-Kerr (2014) and Sraboni et al. (2014) showed that the diets of households in Malawi and in Bangladesh benefit from a diverse agricultural production, including livestock. The distance to markets also seems to be correlated with food security (Ahmed et al. 2009).

Also, nonfarm activities determine the food security status of rural households. They provide important opportunities for diversifying income sources, smoothing consumption, or overcoming imperfections in credit markets (Ruben and van den Berg 2001). There is evidence on this, e.g., for Nigeria (Babatunde and Qaim 2010), Ghana (Owusu, Abdulai, and Abdul-

Rahman 2011), and Malawi (Pankomera, Houssou, and Zeller 2009).

In summary, the review of literature on the drivers of food insecurity shows that information on resource endowments, asset positions, human capital, and general infrastructural conditions of households as well as individual characteristics must be available if one wants to better understand food insecurity conditions. Hence, in order to design effective ex-ante strategies and food security policies, food security assessments—however sophisticated and detailed these may be—are not sufficient.

Overall, it appears that existing datasets for food security have severe limitations as such data is mostly of a short-term and cross-section nature. While detailed indicators have been developed, past data collection efforts in food security often lack other information that can help to explain why people are food insecure at present or face the risk of food insecurity. Also, most of the indicators are static and unidimensional and thus are of little value for generating a better understanding of the causes of food security.

Case Studies

The present four case studies further explore the role of certain drivers and causes of food insecurity in the context of Southeast Asia by making use of some of the above-mentioned indicators. The results of the case studies confirm that food security assessments are often incomplete as they do not take into account the multidimensional facets of food insecurity. Our case studies highlight additional important drivers by disaggregating some of the above-mentioned causes (case studies 1 and 3) and stress the importance of the time dimension (case studies 2 and 4). These insights need to be considered when constructing databases for food security assessments.

The four case studies all draw on own comprehensive survey data. For the first two case studies, we use panel data of the DFG FOR 756 project on vulnerability to poverty in Thailand and Vietnam funded by the German Research Foundation (DFG).[1] The data were collected among some 4,000 rural households in both countries in 2007, 2008, and 2010. In this project, a comprehensive survey with four panel waves has been carried out in six provinces of the two countries.[2] The provinces were purposively selected based on criteria such as low per capita income, importance of agriculture, generally risky conditions because of remoteness, and poor infrastructure. In Thailand, the three provinces are Nakhon Phanom, Ubon Ratchathani, and Buriram; all belonging

---

[1] The DFG FOR 756 is the name of a project of a research group which was funded by the German Research Foundation (DFG). For further information, see www.vulnerability-Asia.de.

[2] Similar panel surveys were carried out in two provinces in Cambodia and Laos.

to the northeastern part of the country which has a long history of poverty and underdevelopment. In Vietnam, the three provinces in the panel include two, i.e. Ha Tinh and Thua Thien Hue that belong to the Central Highlands. These two provinces also border the South China Sea. The third province, Dak Lak is land-locked and belongs to the Southern part of the country.

The remaining two case studies use data from Stung Treng, the Northern Province in Cambodia. The comprehensive household survey conducted in 2013 aimed at measuring vulnerability to poverty and food insecurity of rural households. The questionnaire and the sampling procedure were designed in line with the above-mentioned DFG FOR 756 project being implemented in Thailand and Vietnam. The total sample size in Stung Treng amounted to ~600 randomly sampled households.

Poverty and nutrition

In this case study, we analyze the relationship between poverty reduction and the nutritional status of children using the WFA. In this case study, we explore the relationship between poverty and food security. In line with the literature, we find that households below the poverty line tend to be more food insecure measured in terms of under nutrition of children. However, food insecurity can still be a problem for households above the poverty line. In Annex 1, we present parameters on individual, household, and village levels for four groups of households in Thailand. Group 1 are poor households

with underweight children, group 2 are poor but do not have underweight children, group 3 are nonpoor but they do have underweight children, and the last group are nonpoor without underweight children.

Some differences can be observed between the four groups, e.g. poor households with underweight children have lower per capita food consumption although they may have the same level of income as compared to poor households with no underweight children. Also, the former have a lower share of agricultural income and rely relatively more on food from natural resources which tend to be more erratic in supply. Such difference can no longer be observed for nonpoor households. Another difference is migration of the child's mother. Poor households with normal weighted children have an 8% higher share of mothers working outside the village. This is also reflected in the time that mothers spend outside the household, i.e., mothers from poor households with normal weighted children spend almost thrice the time away. In nonpoor households such differences are smaller. A major factor seems to be assets. Poor households with underweight children have only about half the assets in value terms compared with their counterfactual group. Again this difference is smaller in absolute and relative terms for the nonpoor groups.

Prenatal condition of children as indicated by the mother's height shows some differences in the poor household group while the mother's education is considerably higher in the nonpoor groups.

Interestingly, no difference can be observed in the food consumption expenditure shares among the four groups which suggest that differences may exist in the quality of food assuming positive income elasticity for food expenditures, i.e., as households get better off, their absolute expenditures on food increase. Also, no difference can be observed in sanitation parameters, neither on household nor village level. However, a marked difference can be observed in children who were reported sick. Also, undernourished children tend to have mothers with fewer years of education.

Marked differences exist between poor and nonpoor households, e.g., in labor allocation, poor households are more agriculturally based and nonpoor households have a higher share of wage employment and small-scale business. Furthermore, differences also exist in sanitary conditions, e.g., nonpoor households have better access to water and better hygienic conditions. Furthermore, poor households tend to live in remote mountainous areas. However, differences between households with underweight and normal weighted children for both income groups (poor and nonpoor) are small. Overall, the shares of undernourished children among poor households are about 1:2, whereas it is about 1:5 in nonpoor households.

Further analysis using this dataset for a Tobit model for the four household groups (Waibel and Hohfeld 2015) showed that the factors that influence nutrition outcomes, measured as Z-scores of the weight-for-age indicator, are poverty status and income, mother's height, mother's education, migration status of the mother, and sanitation status of the household. Most importantly, regression coefficients of respective variables differ by poverty status. Hence, nonmonetary factors are important entry points to reduce undernutrition and, therefore, monetary poverty reduction is not a sufficient condition for eliminating food insecurity. This finding is further underlined by a prediction of future undernutrition rates based on the regressions. Even under the assumption of high growth, income growth alone will not be able to reduce undernutrition to a level of low severity until the year 2030 (Waibel and Hohfeld 2015).

Impact of food prices on food consumption shares

This second case study shows the impact of food prices on food consumption shares. From September 2006 to June 2008, the international prices of food commodities increased dramatically, driving the food price index to an unprecedented peak since 1975. Compared to 2005, the food price index increased by ~80%, driven mainly by increasing cereal prices, which increased by 230%.

In Figure 1, the effect of food prices on the distributions of food consumption shares are shown for rural households in Thailand and Vietnam using the same panel data from the six provinces as described previously. The data in Figure 1 show the frequency distribution of household food consumption shares in 2007 and 2010, i.e., before and after the food price and economic crisis. The data from some 4,000 households are taken from the consumption module of the household questionnaire. As shown, after the economic crisis, the distributions shifted to the right for both countries.

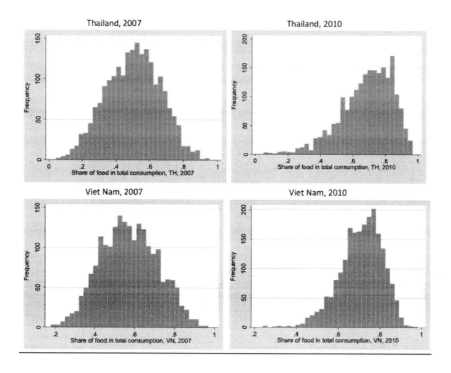

Figure 1: Shares in food consumption before and after food price crisis, Thailand and Vietnam

Source: Waibel and Hohfeld (2015)

This indicates that the majority of rural households had to allocate a much higher share of their consumption expenditures to food. The effect was stronger in Vietnam where the mode shifted to ~80%, whereas it increased to >60% in Thailand.

Relating these observations to the data on poverty and consumption shows that, in spite of a decline in poverty, adjustments in food consumption became necessary and, therefore, consequences for nutrition are likely.

While this brief case study does not use any detailed or in-depth food consumption indicators (as summarized in Annex Table 1), it shows that a consumption module is an important component of any food security database.

Table 2. Headcount ratio with and without environmental income in terms of both income and consumption poverty in Cambodia (2013)

Livelihood cluster	Income poverty (USD 1.25 PPP)				Consumption poverty			
	With environmental income		Without environmental income		With environmental consumption		Without environmental consumption	
	Estimate (%)	Std. dev (%)	Estimate (%)	Std. dev (%)	Estimate (%)	Std. dev (%)	Estimate (%)	Std. dev (%)
Cluster 1	39	49	55	50	38	49	52	50
Cluster 2	30	46	69	46	29	45	47	50
Cluster 3	29	45	33	47	13	34	18	38
Average	33	47	53	50	27	45	40	49

Note: definition of clusters: cluster 1: farming and low-skilled jobs; cluster 2: farming and environmental extraction; cluster 3: farming and self-employment or high-skilled jobs.
Source: based on Nguyen et al. (2015)

Environmental income and household food security

This case study from Cambodia[3] highlights the importance of the natural resource base as an income source for certain livelihood activities of rural households. It is motivated by the fact that inhabitants from Stung Treng are strongly affected by environmental degradation. This is confirmed from the survey with 98% of the households reporting a loss in forest resources, ~90% a decline in wild animals, and 86% depleting fish stocks (Bühler et al. 2015a; 2015b). The unequal access to livelihood activities related to the natural resource base is one of the underlying causes of food insecurity. To identify which households might be especially affected by environmental degradation, 580 households were classified into 3 livelihood clusters: (1) farming and low-skilled jobs, (2) farming and environmental extraction, and (3) farming and self-employment or high-skilled jobs (Nguyen et al. 2015).

We have calculated (1) the headcount ratio (poverty) using either USD 1.25 PPP per capita per day and (2) the FCS with and without natural

[3] We thank Thanh T. Nguyen, Leibniz University Hannover, for compiling this data as an add-on to the paper from Nguyen et al. (2015).

resources. Environmental income derives from the extraction of natural resources including fishing, hunting, and collecting.

In terms of income poverty, excluding environmental income would increase the headcount ratio of the whole sample from 33% to 53% (Table 2). The most affected would be the households in cluster 2 since their livelihood activities depend more on environmental extraction; their headcount ratio increases from 30% to 69%. In contrast, households from cluster 1 would be relatively less affected (increase from 39% to 55%). Similarly, in terms of consumption poverty, if we exclude the natural resources used for home consumption, the overall headcount ratio changes from 27% to 40%. However, in this case the headcount ratio would be larger for households in cluster 1 than 2. Overall, this example shows that environmental income is a major component of poverty reduction and food security and environmental degradation a major threat.

With respect to the FCS, it can be seen from Table 3 that natural resources contribute quite a lot to the high values of the FCS, e.g., in terms of fish, meat, or vegetable. Again, if we exclude the contribution of natural resources, the FCS decreases significantly.

Table 3: FCS with and without natural resources in Cambodia (2013)

Food item	Livelihood clusters			Whole sample
	1	2	3	
Staples	13.9	13.9	14.0	14.0
Roots	0.4	0.7	0.9	0.6
Pulses	2.8	4.0	4.9	3.8
Fruits	2.6	3.5	3.2	3.1
Vegetable	5.1	5.3	5.4	5.3
Fish	22.3	23.5	22.0	22.6
Meat	5.4	6.2	8.9	6.7
Eggs	4.4	3.4	6.0	4.6
Milk	0.3	0.2	1.2	0.5
Oil	1.7	1.8	2.0	1.8
Sugar	2.9	2.8	3.0	2.9
FCS with natural resources	**61.8**	**65.5**	**71.6**	**65.9**
FCS without natural resources	**46.9**	**41.4**	**61.7**	**49.6**

Note: definition of clusters: cluster 1: farming and low-skilled jobs; cluster 2: farming and environmental extraction; cluster 3: farming and self-employment or high-skilled jobs.
Source: based on Nguyen et al. (2015)

In Table 4, we classify the FCS into three groups, namely (1) poor, (2) borderline, and (3) acceptable. We then find that the number and share of households from clusters 1 and 2 in the poor and borderline food consumption groups are very similar if natural resources are excluded.

In sum, this case study from Cambodia highlights (1) the importance of natural resources to poverty reduction and/or food security and (2) that different indicators lead to different findings.

Table 4: Number and share (per total sample of 580 households (% in brackets)) of households classified into three food consumption groups with and without natural resources in Cambodia (2013)

| | Food consumption groups | | | | | | Total number of households |
| | Poor (FCS ≤21) | | Borderline (21<FCS ≤35) | | Acceptable (FCS >35) | | |
	With	Without	With	Without	With	Without	
Cluster 1	0 (0.0)	25 (4.3)	3 (0.5)	41 (7.1)	218 (37.6)	155 (26.7)	221 (38.1)
Cluster 2	0 (0.0)	28 (4.8)	7 (1.2)	42 (7.2)	178 (30.7)	115 (19.8)	185 (31.9)
Cluster 3	1 (0.2)	8 (1.4)	2 (0.3)	17 (2.9)	171 (29.5)	149 (25.7)	174 (30.0)
Total	1 (0.2)	61 (10.5)	12 (2.1)	100 (17.2)	567(97.8)	419 (72.2)	580 (100)

Note: definition of clusters: cluster 1: farming and low-skilled jobs; cluster 2: farming and environmental extraction; cluster 3: farming and self-employment or high-skilled jobs.
Source: based on Nguyen et al. (2015)

Shocks and coping strategies

This case study from Stung Treng province in Cambodia shows that shocks influence the food security situation and livelihood strategies of households. Our household dataset which has been already described at the beginning of this section includes information on agricultural, economic, demographic, and social shocks as perceived at the household level over the preceding year.

Agricultural shocks such as floods, droughts, or storms, but also livestock diseases and crop failures are the most common shocks in Stung Treng (Table 5). They account for slightly more than half (54%) of all reported shocks and relate especially to drought and livestock diseases (69%). Two thirds of the agricultural shocks are perceived to be of medium to high severity. Demographic shocks including events such as birth, death, illness, and accidents of household members also appear to play a major role. In total, households reported 246 of those shocks accounting for more than one third of the total shocks reported. Notably, illnesses make up 83% of this shock type. Economic shocks such as price fluctuations and theft only account for 8% of the total shocks, but nevertheless their impact is perceived as being very high. Social and other shocks—due to weddings or funerals or in case of conflicts with neighbors or relatives—have been hardly reported. This finding is supported by the estimated losses in terms of income and assets as well as extra expenditure associated with the different shock types. As Figures 2a and b show, the high impact of social and

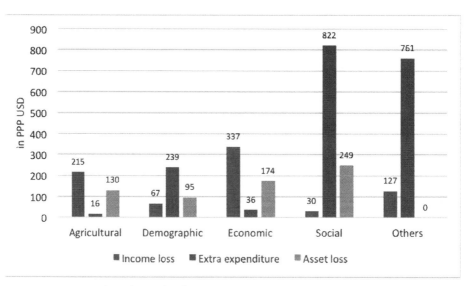

Figure 2a: Average loss from shocks by category (in PPP USD)
Source: Bühler et al. (2015b)

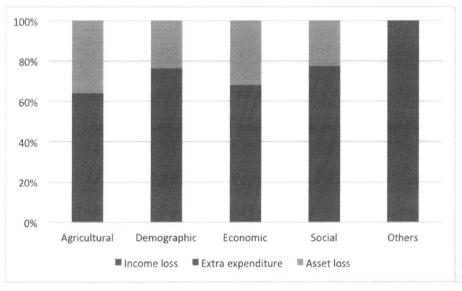

Figure 2b: Average loss from shocks by category (in %)
Source: Bühler et al. (2015b)

other shocks is mainly due to high extra expenditures, especially for medical treatments. However, since the frequency of these two categories is low, the overall impact of these shocks is relatively low. Both the share and the average value of extra expenditures from demographic shocks exceed the income and asset losses associated with agricultural and economic shocks. Economic shocks are associated with ~60% income loss. But again, the frequency of economic shocks is comparatively low.

Households were also asked about the coping strategies they employ after they have been affected by a shock. In 57% of the cases, households responded that they did not adopt any specific coping strategy (Table 5). Households use economic coping activities mainly to counteract the effect

of economic and agricultural shocks. These include activities such as labor and crop diversification, reducing inputs for production, or increasing natural resource extraction. The most frequently used coping strategy to offset particularly demographic shocks is to rely on borrowing or own savings. Since demographic shocks are mostly related to health issues, it is straightforward that in these cases, money is needed fast to pay for medical treatment. Grants appear to only play a role in the context of social shocks. Furthermore, households indicate that they do not change their food consumption habits to cope with any shock. Demographic coping activities such as migrating or sending children or adult family members to live with relatives and friends are also negligible (Bühler et al. 2015b).

Table 5. Coping activity by shock type

	Shock type					
	Agricultural	**Demographic**	**Economic**	**Social**	**Others**	**Total**
Shock frequency (no.)	359	246	54	4	6	669
Share without coping (%)	71	36	65	0	50	57
Type of coping activity (%)						
Economic (less inputs, etc.)	60	17	68	0	0	36
Demographic (migration)	1	1	0	0	0	1
Selling assets	10	20	5	25	33	16
Borrowing and savings	25	51	21	50	67	40
Grants	2	8	5	25	0	6
Change food consumption	2	1	0	0	0	1

Source: Bühler et al. (2015b)

In sum, the impact and frequency of different types of shocks need to be considered to be able to capture food security in an adequate and sustainable way. A shock module is an important component in a food security database. Furthermore, information about the coping activities help to identify entry points to support the affected rural households.

Data Requirements for Food Security Assessment

In this section, we discuss components of datasets which are essential for a better understanding of food security. As visualized by the case studies presented in the previous section, datasets need to be comprehensive and of longer term.

While comprehensive data allow us to better understand the four dimensions of food security (availability, access, utilization, and stability), only long-term panel data allow us to analyze the dynamics of food security hence satisfy the risk dimension of food security.

Essential parameters

Household surveys generally try to attain information and knowledge on socioeconomic household characteristics, welfare measures of households including income, assets, and consumption but also livelihood strategies. Hardeweg, Klasen, and Waibel (2013) pointed out that three additional issues are most critical in household surveys when studying vulnerability to poverty. We submit that the same points which are important for understanding the future risks also hold for food insecurity. First, the definition of households is essential. It has been found that a wider definition is preferable in the rural context as members of the household might have migrated but still feel being part of the household and thus sending remittances to support the household's access to nutritious food over time. This is particularly important for targeting social protection programs (Gödecke and Waibel 2015). Furthermore, Nguyen, Raabe, and Grote (2015b) confirm that migration is a livelihood support strategy for rural households.

Second, the incorporation of a module on shocks with information on type of shock, shock severity, timing, and coping strategies of households is considered as being essential as it allows us to capture the dynamics of food security assessments. Shocks do affect households with implications for their food security. Thus, climate change and HIV/AIDS, for example, are known to have impact on food security (Rosegrant and Cline 2013; Badolo and Kinda 2012).

Third, the time dimension is critical, especially as shocks influence the stability dimension of food security. But also seasons have a significant effect on food security with households consistently worse off during monsoon season as evidenced in Bangladesh (Hillbruner and Egan 2008).

Many household panel datasets already exist in developing and transition countries (Baulch 2011). However, most of them started in the early 1990s and many of them have been discontinued so that a huge gap exists in longer term multi-purpose panel household surveys in developing and emerging economies.

Furthermore, some of the existing panels were not only of short duration, but also had low sample sizes, a narrow geographic focus, or were designed for very specific purposes and thus did not allow intercountry comparisons. Alinovi, Mane, and Romano (2009) admit that most papers on food security are descriptive and lack panel data. They mostly take an ex-post view because of the multidimensionality of food security models. Finally, none of these surveys are focused on rural conditions where the existence of poverty and food security is widespread and persistent over long periods of time.

Against the backdrop of the existing panel databases in developing countries, we present our long-term panel project which tries to address the above-mentioned shortcomings of other panel datasets. Our long-term panel project has been designed for food security assessments as we will describe more in detail in the next subsection.

Long-term panel project

The long-term panel project builds on the structure and the collaborations established by the Research Group DFG FOR 756 funded by the German Research Foundation. It continues and further advances the existing high-quality panel database from Thailand and Vietnam. Until to date, household and village surveys have been carried out in three selected regions in Thailand and Vietnam in 2007, 2008, 2010, and 2013, i.e., four panel waves. In addition, in 2010, a complementary migrant tracking survey of 1,000 migrants in Ho Chi Minh City and Bangkok was carried out. In 2011, all panel households in the provinces of Ubon Ratchathani (Thailand) and Hué (Vietnam) were surveyed again to capture medium-term agricultural effects. An extension of the panel by another six waves (until 2023) can make this database truly unique in terms of the length and continuity and the depth and scope of the inquiries and thus allowing to address many long-term development questions including nutrition and food insecurity.

In order to meet the objective of conducting comprehensive food security studies that can capture all four food security dimensions, in principle two questionnaires are needed: a village and a comprehensive household survey. The village questionnaire collects information on the village characteristics, such as its location and physical and social infrastructure, and the socioeconomic and demographic profile of the village (e.g., age structure, welfare status of households, unemployment rates, and major income sources) strategies. The household questionnaire includes a range of modules which are shown in Table 6. Although the questionnaire has originally been developed for research on vulnerability to poverty it can contribute to food security studies through many of its sections. Adding specific modules on in-depth food security indicators would be possible and has in fact been implemented for the Cambodia and Laos panel surveys. Also, the survey can be complemented by selected focus group discussions for example to determine the Coping Strategies Index (CSI), as suggested by Maxwell and Caldwell (2008), and even randomized control trials related to food security.

Our long-term panel project for Thailand and Vietnam appears unique and valuable in several respects (see also Klasen and Waibel 2013). First, its sampling design facilitates comparisons of countries, regions, and provinces. Second, the sample size at provincial level is larger than any of the existing panels and the period spanned will be among the longest of any survey study. Third, the database allows comparisons of individual households and to some extent also of individuals within households. It consistently includes migrants and, thus, covers an important driver of household dynamics in emerging market economies. Fourth, the survey instrument contains all aspects of the living standard measures and adds comprehensive modules on shocks, risks, expectations, and subjective assessments of welfare. Fifth, it has a very low attrition rate due to an incentive structure that promotes ownership through active participation of the scientists in the data collection process and thus closely links data collection with research output.

The long-term panel data project will therefore provide unique opportunities to advance scientific research on poverty, vulnerability, and food security. The value-added of the project emanates both from its long-term nature and the richness of information that allow for a good tracking of households' expectations and actions. It will permit the analysis of long and medium term, dynamic, and inter-temporal dimensions that is rarely possible with existing datasets, including the currently existing four waves of the FOR756 panel. The panel datasets can help to advance research related to food

Table 6. Modules of household questionnaire for panel database to measure vulnerability to poverty and its link to food security

Questionnaire module		Variables	Contribution to food security studies
1	General survey information	Geographic location, household headship, decision making	
2	Household characteristics	Size, composition and dynamics, education, health conditions; diversity of the household production system	Anthropometric measures
3	Shocks experienced during past five years and perceived risks for the next 5 years	Type, timing, duration, scope, severity, consequence, ex post coping measures, covariance, subjective assessment of risk and well-being; type, frequency, severity, consequence of expected risks and ex ante mitigation measures; seasonal and permanent labor migration	Causes of food insecurity and coping strategies
4	Land, agriculture and natural resources	Land size and ownership status, land value, crop and livestock technology and production, self-consumption, productivity, costs, returns, timing and extent of natural resource extraction	Food availability
5	Off-farm employment including wage labor	Type, contractual arrangements, location, travel costs, job acquisition costs, duration of work, wage and fringe benefits	Food access
6	Non-farm self-employment including cottage industries	Type, investment, costs and returns	Food access
7	Borrowing, lending, public and other transfers and insurance	Type, sources, contractual arrangements, conditions amounts, payment frequencies	Food access and stability
8	Household consumption	Food and non-food items, other expenditures	Food access and utilization
9	Assets	Purchase value depreciation and service life	Food access and coping capacity

Source: based on Hardeweg, Klasen, and Waibel (2013).

security by providing long-term and vulnerability-specific data to empirically test general theoretical approaches in research areas which are all entwined with food security such as: poverty dynamics; risks and behavioral aspects in development; demography, gender and inequality; nutrition and poverty; finance and development; regional development; labor and migration; middle income trap; and climate, environment and agriculture.

Summary and Conclusion

Given the need for research to better understand the determinants and drivers of food security in order to contribute to a long-term solution of the problem this article promotes the notion of advancing and complementing panel databases that allow undertaking in-depth and causal analyses in food security.

We started out from the findings that the literature on food security assessments has evolved rapidly, but that each concept or indicator of food security has its own shortcomings; in addition, individual measures fail to capture all four important dimensions of food security, and rather complement than substitute each other. Our case studies were intended to show that results of food security assessments can differ depending on the type of indicator used.

We conclude however that although specific food security indicators remain useful for international organizations to undertake quick analyses especially in situations of emergency, more rigorous research is needed to achieve food security on the

long run. Generally such research must adopt a comprehensive approach which allows identifying and analyzing the determinants of food security. There are two reasons for this. First, only through a better understanding of the determinants will it be possible to help to prevent food emergencies. Second, such a comprehensive approach allows considering the context and the interplay of factors which are important.

We further suggest that much could be gained if food security research will be joined with research on vulnerability to poverty. Hence data collection on food security must be not only comprehensive but also become part of broader livelihood and vulnerability studies. This has been highlighted through our four case studies. These showed that households' livelihood strategies and different types of shocks are intertwined with food security. Food security assessments also need to be based on long-term panel datasets, as only these allow taking into account the dynamics of food security and hereby capture the risk dimension of food security.

Against this background, we presented our long-term panel data project for Thailand and Vietnam which we believe is unique and valuable also for food security assessments. These data are available for the worldwide research community dealing with socio-economic questions of development. The project, for example allows: (i) comparisons of countries, regions and provinces, (ii) assures representativeness for potentially food insecure rural populations as its sample size at provincial level is larger than in any of the existing panels, (iii) especially allows to capture the risk dimension of food security as the period covered will be very long by the standard of other scientific panel datasets, (iv) the database allows comparisons of individual households and to some extent also of individuals within households including migrant members, and (v) the survey instrument contains all aspects of the living standard measures and adds comprehensive modules on shocks, risks, expectations and subjective assessments of welfare.

Although the collection of data in remote rural areas of poor countries is challenging, data quality is crucial in order to advance research on the economics of food security. This requires the application of modern survey management tools that must include advanced information and communication technology (IT) solutions as well as a good blend of participation, motivation and supervision.

While the panel database exists for the emerging market economies Thailand and Vietnam, a similar long term panel is also of relevance to food insecure countries in other continents, namely in Sub Saharan Africa (SSA) where more research on the causes of food security is needed. SSA is the region with the highest rates of food insecurity and poverty; this is especially true for the rural areas. Understanding the dynamics of rural poverty and food insecurity is thus detrimental to develop effective strategies for a long-term reduction of poverty and inequality. Overall, we suggest that by incorporating food security research into long-term panel data projects, a much better understanding of this problem and better solutions can be reached.

References

ADB. 2014. *Poverty in Asia: A Deeper Look. Key Indicators for Asia and the Pacific.* Special Chapter. Manila: Asian Development Bank.

Ahmed, A., R. Hill, L. Smith, and T. Frankenberger. 2009. "The Poorest and Hungry: Characteristics and Causes." In *The Poorest and Hungry—Assessments, Analyses, and Actions*, eds. J. von Braun, R.V. Hill, and R. Pandya-Lorch. Washington, DC: International Food Policy Research Institute.

Alinovi, L., E. Mane and D. Romano (2009): Measuring household resilience to food insecurity: application to Palestinian households. Working paper, EC-FAO Food Security Programme, Food and Agriculture Organization of the United Nations, Rome.

Babatunde, R.O., and M. Qaim. 2010. "Impact of Off-Farm Income on Food Security and Nutrition in Nigeria." *Food Policy* 35(4): 303–311.

Badolo, F., and S.R. Kinda. 2012. "Climatic Shocks and Food Security in Developing Countries." MPRA Paper No.43006. https://mpra.ub.uni-muenchen.de/43006 (accessed November 2015).

Barrett, C.B. 2010. "Measuring Food Insecurity." *Science* 327: 825–828.

Baulch, B. (2011): Why Poverty Persists: Poverty Dynamics in Asia and Africa. Cheltenham: Edward Elgar Publishing.

Bogale, A. 2012. "Vulnerability of Smallholder Rural Households to Food Insecurity in Eastern Ethiopia." *Food Security* 4: 581–591.

Bühler, D., U. Grote, R. Hartje, B. Ker, D.T. Lam, L.D. Nguyen, T.T. Nguyen, and K. Ton. 2015a. "Rural Livelihood Strategies in Cambodia: Evidence from a household survey in Stung Treng." ZEF Working Paper Series No.137. Bonn: Center for Development Research (ZEF).

Bühler, D., U. Grote, R. Hartje, B. Ker, D.T. Lam, L.D. Nguyen, T.T. Nguyen, and K. Ton. 2015b. *Impact of Shocks on Livelihood Clusters in Stung Treng.* Mimeo: Institute for Environmental Economics and World Trade, Leibniz University Hannover.

Carletto, C., A. Zezza, and R. Banerjee. 2013. "Towards Better Measurement of Household Food Security: Harmonizing Indicators and The Role of Household Surveys." *Global Food Security* 2: 30–40.

Coates, J. 2013. "Build it Back Better: Deconstructing Food Security for Improved Measurement and Action." *Global Food Security* 2: 188–194.

de Haen, H., S. Klasen, and M. Qaim. 2011. "What Do We Really Know? Metrics for Food Insecurity and Undernutrition." *Food Policy* 36: 760–769.

Devereux, S. 2006. *Distinguishing Between Chronic and Transitory Food Insecurity in Emergency Needs Assessments.* Rome: World Food Programme.

FAO. 1996. *Rome Declaration on World Food Security and World Food Summit Plan of Action.* Rome: Food and Agriculture Organization of the United Nations (FAO).

FAO. 2006. *Food Security. Policy Brief, Issue 2, June.* Rome: Food and Agriculture Organization.

FAO. 2011. *World Livestock (2011): Livestock in Food Security.* Rome: Food and Agricultural Organization of the United Nations (FAO).

Fuwa, N. 2000. "A Note On The Analysis of Female Headed Households in Developing Countries." Technical Bulletin of the Faculty of Horticulture of Chiba University, 125–138.

Gödecke, T., and H. Waibel. 2015. "Does The Underlying Definition of Household Impair Programme Targeting?" *Journal of Development Effectiveness.* doi: 10.1080/19439342.2015.1079793.

Hardeweg, B., Klasen, and H. Waibel. 2013. "Establishing a Database for Vulnerability Assessment." In *Vulnerability to Poverty: Theory, Measurement and Determinants, With Case Studies From Thailand and Vietnam*, eds. S. Klasen, and H. Waibel. Palgrave, 360p.

Hart, T.G.B. 2009. "Exploring Definitions of Food Insecurity and Vulnerability: Time to Refocus Assessments." *Agrekon* 8(4): 362–383.

Headey, D., and O. Ecker. 2013. "Rethinking the Measurement of Food Security: From First Principles to Best Practice." *Food Security* 5(3): 327–343.

Hillbruner, C., and R. Egan. 2008. "Seasonality, Household Food Security, and Nutritional Status on Dinajpur, Bangladesh." *Food Nutrition Bulletin* 29(3): 221–231.

Hoddinott, J. 1999. "Choosing Outcome Indicators for Household Food Security." Technical Guide #7. Washington, DC: International Food Policy Research Institute (IFPRI).

Hoddinott, J., and Y. Yohannes. 2002. "Dietary Diversity as a Food Security Indicator." FCND Discussion Paper No.136. Washington, DC: International Food Policy Research Institute.

Jones, A., F.M. Ngure, G. Pelto, and S.L. Young. 2013. "What Are We Assessing When We Measure Food Security? A Compendium and Review of Current Metrics." *Advances in Nutrition* 4: 481–505.

Jones, A., A. Shrinivas, and R. Bezner-Kerr. 2014. "Farm Production Diversity is Associated with Greater Household Dietary Diversity in Malawi: Findings From Nationally Representative Data." *Food Policy* 46: 1–12.

Kassie, M., S.W. Ndiritu, and J. Stage. 2014. "What Determines Gender Inequality in Household Food Security in Kenya? Application of Exogenous Switching Treatment Regression." *World Development* 56: 153–171.

Klasen, S. and H. Waibel 2013. Vulnerability to Poverty Theory, Measurement and Determinants. Hardcover, Palgrave Macmillan. Maxwell, D., and R. Caldwell. 2008. *A Tool For Rapid Measurement of Household Food Security and The Impact of Food Aid Programs in Humanitarian Emergencies. Field Methods Manual*. Second Edition. CARE International.

Maxwell, S., and T. Frankenberger. 1992. "Household Food Security: Concepts, Indicators, Measurements." A Technical Review. UNICEF/IFAD, New York/Rome.

Maxwell, S., and M. Smith. 1992. "Household Food Security: A Conceptual Review." In S. Maxwell & T.R. Frankenberger, Eds. *Household Food Security: Concepts, Indicators, Measurements: A Technical Review*. New York and Rome: UNICEF and IFAD.

Maxwell, D., B. Vaitla, and J. Coates. 2014. "How Do Indicators of Household Food Insecurity Measure Up? An Empirical Comparison From Ethiopia." *Food Policy* 47 (2014): 107-116.

Nguyen, T.T., T.L. Do, D. Bühler, R. Hartje, and U. Grote. 2015a. "Rural livelihoods and Environmental Resource Dependence in Cambodia." *Ecological Economics* 120: 282–295.

Nguyen, L., K. Raabe, and U. Grote. 2015b. "Rural–Urban Migration, Household Vulnerability, and Welfare in Vietnam." *World Development* 71: 79–93.

Owusu, V., A. Abdulai, and S. Abdul-Rahman. 2011. "Non-Farm Work and Food Security Among Farm Households in Northern Ghana." *Food Policy* 36: 108–118.

Pankomera, P., N. Houssou, and M. Zeller. 2009. "Household Food Security in Malawi: Measurements, Determinants and Policy Review." Paper Presented at the *Conference on International Research on Food Security, Natural Resource Management and Rural Development*, Tropentag, October 6–8.

Quisumbing, A., L. Brown, H. Feldstein, L. Haddad, and C. Pena. 1995. "Women: The Key to Food Security." Food Policy Report. Washington, DC: International Food Policy Research Institute.

Rosegrant, M.W., and S.A. Cline. 2013. "Global Food Security: Challenges and Policies." *Science* 302 (5652): 1917–1919.

Ruben, R. and M. van den Berg. 2001, "Nonfarm Employment and Poverty Alleviation of Rural Farm Households in Honduras" *World Development* 29 (3): 549-560.

Sraboni, E., H.J. Malapit, A.R. Quisumbing, and A.U. Ahmed. 2014. "Women's Empowerment in Agriculture: What Role for Food Security in Bangladesh?" *World Development* 61: 11–52.

Svedberg, P. 2011. "How Many People are Malnourished?" *Annual Review of Nutrition* 31: 263–283.

Swindale, A., and P. Bilinsky. 2006. "Development of a Universally Applicable Household Food Insecurity Measurement Tool: Process, Current Status, and Outstanding Issues." *Journal of Nutrition* 136(5): 1449–1452.

UN. 2015. "Sustainable Development Knowledge Platform." https://sustainable development.un.org/post2015/transform ingourworld.

Von Braun, J., H. Bouis, S. Kumar, and R. Pandya-Lorch. 1992. *Improving Food Security of the Poor: Concept, Policy, and Programs*. Washington, DC: International Food Policy Research Institute (IFPRI).

Waibel, H., and L. Hohfeld. 2015. "Poverty and Nutrition: A Case Study of Rural Households in Thailand and Viet Nam." In *The Asian "Poverty Miracle": Impressive Accomplishments or Incomplete Achievements?*, eds. G. Wan and J. Silber. Edward Elgar, Cheltenham (forthcoming).

WFP. 2009a. *Emergency Food Security Assessment Handbook*. Second Edition. Rome: World Food Programme.

WFP. 2009b. *Comprehensive Food Security & Vulnerability Analysis Guidelines*. First Edition. Rome: World Food Programme.

WFP. 2008a. *Food Consumption Analysis. Calculation and Use of the Food Consumption Score in Food Security Analysis*. Rome: World Food Programme.

WFP. 2008b. *Kingdom of Cambodia: Comprehensive Food Security and Vulnerability Analysis*. Rome: World Food Programme.

WHO. 1986. "Use and Interpretation of Anthropometric Indicators of Nutritional Status." *Bulletin of the World Health Organization* 64(6): 929–941.

Wiesmann, D., L. Bassett, T. Benson, and J. Hoddinott. 2009. "Validation of the World Food Programme's Food Consumption Score and Alternative Indicators of Household Food Security." IFPRI Discussion Paper 00870. Washington, DC: International Food Policy Research Institute (IFPRI).

Appendix 1

Comparison of children by poverty ($2 poverty line) and nutritional status (WFA), Thailand 2007–2010

Groups	(1) Poor and underweight	(2) Poor and no underweight	(3) Nonpoor and underweight	(4) Nonpoor and no underweight
Income				
Income per capita and month (PPP $)	22.53	22.91	165.63	185.63
Share agricultural income*	0.41	0.53	0.21	0.22
Share natural resources income*	0.09	0.07	0.04	0.03
Food Consumption per capita and month (PPP$)	41.88	49.09	72.90	68.83
Share food of total consumption	0.60	0.62	0.63	0.60
Share households with small-scale business	0.19	0.20	0.33	0.34
Child				
Share of children sick	0.05	0.05	0.01	0.04
Share of girls	0.44	0.46	0.42	0.45
Mother				
M_height (cm)	153.89	156.07	156.76	157.82
M_edu (years)	7.02	7.30	8.60	9.31
Share M_migrant	0.15	0.23	0.17	0.18
Household				
HHsize	5.28	5.32	5.11	5.27
Dependency ratio	2.18	2.05	2.01	1.89
Migmonth_other	1.03	2.70	0.96	2.06
Share agricultural worker	0.59	0.62	0.52	0.49
Share wage worker	0.05	0.05	0.10	0.10
Share business worker	0.36	0.33	0.38	0.41
Share priv. toilet	0.91	0.95	0.97	0.97
Share tapwater	0.25	0.27	0.23	0.30
Value assets per capita (PPP $)	717.04	1364.20	1648.86	2014.91
Value livestock per capita (PPP $)	195.47	179.28	201.43	241.39
Land per capita (ha)	0.67	0.57	0.73	0.76
Village				
VP sanitation	75.69	75.2	80.34	77.25
Vpub Water	0.88	0.88	0.91	0.90
Distance market	17.73	19.96	18.27	16.79
Distance hospital	23.43	23.70	21.05	21.54
N	97	586	132	831

*negative crop/natural resource incomes excluded.

Source: Waibel and Hohfeld 2015.

World Food Policy - Volume 2 Issue 2/Volume 3 Issue 1, Fall 2015/Spring 2016

Income Diversity and Poverty Transitions: Evidence from Vietnam

Van Q. Tran[A]

The large share of the population in rural areas of the developing world has been diversifying their livelihood to nonagricultural activities. However, the amount of the literature that discusses the possible effects of the diversity on a household's well-being is still limited. This study contributes to this strand of the literature by investigating the effects of income diversity on poverty transitions. The analysis is based on household panel data collected in the 2000s from Vietnam and applied to a multinomial logit model. The results show that households with better access to markets are more able to diversify their income sources to nonagricultural activities and the diversity is helpful for a household to escape poverty or to avoid falling into poverty.

Keywords: *income diversity, poverty transitions, nonagricultural income sources, Vietnam*

JEL classification: I32, O13, P36, R11

Introduction

The dynamics of poverty have been one of the central issues in development economics. There has been a great deal of theoretical studies (Cappellari and Jenkins 2004; Carter and Barret 2006) and empirical studies (McCulloch and Baulch 1999; Glewwe, Gragnolati, and Zaman 2000; Woolard and Klasen 2005; Justino, Litchfield, and Pham 2008) that discuss the transitions into and out of poverty using different approaches and country cases. They have identified the characteristics of a household, the private and public assets a household possesses, the changes in macroeconomic condition such as trade reform, inflation, and economic crisis on the dynamics of poverty.

In fact, the majority of the poor lives in rural areas and engages in agricultural activities. Also, the large share of the rural population is diversifying their income sources to nonagricultural activities that are usually

[A] University of Economics and Law, Vietnam National University

doi: 10.18278/wfp.2.2.3.1.7

of higher returns and consequently making them better off. Studies by De Janvry, Fafchamps, and Sadoulet (1991) and Kinsey, Burger, and Gunning (1998) indicate that income diversification is not only positively correlated with wealth but also with an increased ability to cope with shocks. Diversification is a way through which rural households insure themselves against the occurrence of such shocks, or, in other words, diversification reduces livelihood vulnerability. This self-insurance can also be seen as a negative function of the availability of social insurance, provided, for example, by the community or family. The better access to social networks and institutions, the less likely a household needs to apply self-insurance systems as the diversification of income portfolios. In contrast, social capital can also foster the ability to participate in many different income activities.

This study aims to contribute to the literature of vulnerability to poverty by examining the relationship between a household's diversity of income sources to nonagricultural activities and its transitions into and out of poverty. The main goal is to identify which households are more able to diversify income sources and if such income diversity makes the household better off or prevents it from falling into poverty.

This study examines these research questions in the context of Vietnam, although the approach can be applied to other developing countries. Vietnam has been one of the most successful countries in the developing world in terms of economic growth and poverty reduction. The rapid economic growth, together with market liberalization and

trade openness that took place during the last two decades, has lifted a large share of the population out of poverty (see Tran, Alkire, and Klasen 2015). Nonetheless, poverty is still a central issue in the country as nearly 43 percent of the population still lives on less than $2 a day (World Bank 2013), and many people earn their living by engaging in agricultural activities. Various population subgroups have benefited less from such development; households in rural areas have made slower progress than those in urban areas (see GSO 2011).

This study uses three waves of a panel surveys from 2007, 2008, and 2010 of more than 2000 rural and peri-urban households from three provinces in Vietnam. The drivers of poverty transitions are investigated via descriptive statistics and empirical results from multinomial logit (MNL) models. The analyses are based on the hypothesis that a household that diversifies its income sources to nonagricultural activities finds it easier to escape poverty than a household that relies its income only on agricultural activities. The findings confirm that an increase in the share of nonagricultural income to total household income is correlated with the advancement of a household's well being. This study is organized as follows. Section 2 describes the household panel data used in the analysis and presents the estimation strategy. Section 3 discusses the results of the MNL models that highlight the relationship between income diversification and household well-being. It also discusses the robustness of the estimation results. Finally, Section 4 concludes with the key messages of this paper.

Empirical Strategy

Data

This study is based on panel household surveys from 2007, 2008, and 2010 from the provinces of Hà Tĩnh (HT), Thừa Thiên Huế (TTH), and Đắk Lắk (DL) in Vietnam for the purpose of the research project "Vulnerability in Southeast Asia" being run by a consortium of German universities and local research institutes (see Klasen and Waibel 2012). The survey covers more than 2000 households located in rural and peri-urban areas in these three provinces. The three provinces have a diversity of agricultural and ecological conditions with mountainous, highland, lowland, and coastal zones. The surveys collect information on household demographics, health, education, economic activities, employment, access to financial markets, public transfers, household expenditures, and assets, and particularly on shocks and risks.

1.1 The Drivers of Poverty Transitions

This study applies an MNL model presented in Wooldridge (2002). Changes in household poverty statuses over a period can be classified into several mutually exclusive outcomes. The MNL model determines the probability that household i experiences one of the mutually exclusive outcomes j. The probability is expressed as

$$(1) \qquad p_{ij} = P\left(Y_i = j\right) = \frac{e^{\beta_j x_i}}{\sum_{k=1}^{J} e^{\beta_k x_i}} \text{ for } j = 0, 1, 2, \dots, J,$$

where Y_i is the outcome experienced by household i, β_k are the set of coefficients to be estimated, and x_i includes a household's covariates and their changes. The model is, however, unidentified since there is more than one solution for that leads to the same probabilities $Y = 0$, $Y =$ 1, $Y = 2,\dots$, $Y = J$. To identify the model, one of the β_j must be set to zero, and all other sets are estimated in relation to that base category. For convenience, β_0 is set to zero; therefore, the above probability function can be written as

$$(2) \quad p_{ij} = P\left(Y_i = j\right) = \frac{e^{\beta_j x_i}}{1 + \sum_{k=1}^{J} e^{\beta_k x_i}}, \text{ for } j = 1, 2, \dots, J \quad \text{and} \quad p_{i0} = P\left(Y_i = 0\right) = \frac{1}{1 + \sum_{k=1}^{J} e^{\beta_k x_i}}$$

From the panel years of 2007, 2008, and 2010, poverty dynamics can be classified into eight categories of (1) being nonpoor in all periods, (2a) poor--poor–nonpoor, (2b) poor–nonpoor–nonpoor, (3a) nonpoor–poor–poor, (3b) nonpoor–nonpoor–poor, (4a) nonpoor–poor–nonpoor, (4b) poor–nonpoor–poor, and (5) being poor in all periods. These eight categories can be grouped into five mutually exclusive outcomes: (1) $J = 4$ and $P(Y = 0)$ is the household's probability of being nonpoor in all periods, $P(Y = 1)$ is the probability of rising (includes categories (2a) and (2b)), $P(Y = 2)$ is the probability of falling (includes categories (3a) and (3b)), and $P(Y = 3)$ is the probability of churning (includes categories (4a) and (4b)), and $P(Y = 4)$ is the probability of being poor in all periods. Thus, the specific model applied in this study when standardizing $\beta_0 = 0$ is expressed as

$$(3) \quad p_{ij} = P\left(Y_i = j\right) = \frac{e^{\beta_j x_i}}{1 + \sum_{k=1}^{4} e^{\beta_k x_i}}, \text{ for } j = 1, 2, 3, 4 \text{ and } \quad p_{i0} = P\left(Y_i = 0\right) = \frac{1}{1 + \sum_{k=1}^{4} e^{\beta_k x_i}}.$$

The (MNL) model will estimate coefficients for four categories relative to the omitted category (being nonpoor in all periods). In order the relationship to make more sense, the results of the (MNL) model are used to predict marginal effects, which measure the conditional probabilities of a change in the regressors on the outcome and are estimated as

$$(4) \quad \frac{\partial p_{ij}}{\partial x_i} = p_{ij}\left(\beta_j - \sum_{k=1}^{4} p_{ik}\beta_k\right).$$

A marginal effect shows the impact of a change in an explanatory variable on the probability of a household being in each of the five categories.

To investigate the dynamics of poverty in Vietnam, I hypothesize that a household's poverty transitions depend on the diversity of income sources, its characteristics, and its head's characteristics.

The measurement of poverty dynamics refers to equivalence scaled[2] income and a Vietnam national poverty line estimated by the Ministry of Labour, Invalids and Social Affairs (MOLISA), which was approximately $1.21[3] a day

---

[1] Equivalence scaled income is calculated by dividing a household's total income by its equivalence size using OECD (1982) scale.

[2] This poverty threshold is measured in purchasing power parity (PPP) price estimated in 2005.

by 2008. Similarly, a household's income is used to measure the diversity from agricultural sources to nonagricultural sources.

Explanatory variables include income diversity and household asset levels. Income diversity is measured by an increase in the share of income from nonagricultural activities to the household's total income over a period. A household's asset is measured by household and individual characteristics as proxies for human capital; land use and asset index represent physical assets. Also, a household's location will be a proxy for the household's access to markets.

Household characteristics are measured by a household's size that counts the number of the household's member. The household's head characteristics include gender, age, ethnicity, and education attainment. In addition, a household's physical assets include quantitative and qualitative items. The quantitative assessment concerns whether the household has: a motorbike, a bike, a television, a radio, a CD player, an electric fan, an electric rice cooker, a fridge, and a mattress. The quality assessment includes: having improved flooring condition, having improved housing condition, having access to improved sanitation facility, and using improved cooking fuel.[3] House size is also included, measured in square meters. These items are included in the estimation of the asset index via principal component analysis. Among the items, motorbike plays an important role (with a weight of 24 percent), and then comes television (10 percent), while the other items are less important, each of which contributes less than 10 percent to the asset index (see Table A.1).

The location of a household includes a dummy variable indicating provincial location. DL is located in the highlands with basalt soil, which is suitable for high-value crops such as coffee, pepper, cashew, and rubber. The population density in the province is also low, allowing households to possess more land than households in the other two provinces. In contrast, HT and TTH are in the coastal area and are frequently hit by storms and floods. These differences make it reasonable to treat DL as a reference.

Income Diversity and Poverty Transitions in Vietnam

The Patterns of Income Diversification

The main income sources of many households were those from agricultural activities. On average, agricultural activities accounted for 40 percent of a household's total income; this share was 50 percent in DL as many households there grew high-value crops such as coffee and pepper.

---

[3] Reference categories: The floor is made of cement or ceramic. The main walls are made of concrete and the roof is made of slates or concrete. The household uses flushed toilet. The household cooks with gas or electricity.

Agricultural activities usually included the crop production of rice, coffee, pepper, and corn, peanut, vegetable, and livestock production of cow, pig, and chicken. On average, a household had slightly more than five agricultural activities that yielded close to Vietnamese Dong (VND) 10 million by 2007, i.e., each activity yielded an average of VND 2 million per year. Over the three-year period, there was an increase of 0.5 activities and income

Table 1 Levels and changes in income sources by population subgroups

Population subgroups	Agricultural activities				Nonagricultural activities			
	Number of activities		Total income (mil. VND)		Number of activities		Total income (mil. VND)	
	Level 2007	Absolute change 2007–2010	Level 2007	Change 2007–2010 (%)	Level 2007	Absolute change 2007–2010	Level 2007	Change 2007–2010 (%)
Total	5.2	0.5	9.6	9.2	1.0	0.1	17.9	22.1
Head has no schooling	4.2	0.6	5.5	−0.6	1.1	0.1	13.1	21.6
Head attains primary school	4.7	0.5	6.9	47.2	1.1	0.1	17.2	−2.4
Middle school and beyond	5.6	0.5	11.4	1.8	1.0	0.1	19.2	29.9
Ethnic minority groups	5.4	0.4	9.2	7.6	0.9	0.1	18.7	26.0
Kinh (majority)	4.1	1.4	11.7	15.5	1.4	0.1	13.9	−4.6
Hà Tĩnh	6.3	0.5	5.2	85.4	0.6	0.2	15.5	39
Thừa Thiên Huế	6.0	−0.6	4.9	−8.9	1.3	0.1	19.7	34
Đắk Lắk	3.7	1.2	16.5	−12.8	1.3	0.1	19.4	3

Notes: Agricultural activities include crops and livestock production. Nonagricultural activities include all other income-generating activities. Income values refer to price level in April 2008. mil. VND refers to million Vietnamese Dong.
Source: Author's calculations from Vulnerability Surveys in Vietnam.

from these activities increased by closed to 10 percent. Nonagricultural activities were usually off-farm employment, self-employment, interest from lending, remittance, and public transfer, etc. On average, a nonagricultural activity yielded closed to VND 18 million by 2007. Over the three years, there was only a little increase of 0.1 activities, but income from this activity rose by 22 percent (see Table 1). These imply that the transition to nonagricultural activities affects positively on a household's income; yet, the transition was relatively slow.

The pattern of income diversity differed from one population subgroup to another. Households in DL had less agricultural activities than their counterparts in HT and TTH, but agricultural activities in the former were of higher value. On average, a household in DL had only less than four agricultural activities and earned closed to VND 17 million from coffee, pepper, and cashew crops, while a household in TTH and HT had more than six agricultural activities by 2007 and earned only approximately VND 5 million. Nonagricultural sectors were not developed in HT, making households there rely more on crops and livestock to generate income.

Among 54 ethnic groups in Vietnam, the Kinh is the majority that accounts for nearly 86 percent of the entire population. They usually live in lowlands, which allows them to have better access to markets and public services, ergo they benefit more from economic growth. On average, a Kinh household had less agricultural income sources and earned more from these than a household of ethnic minority groups did; the earlier also made a faster increase in the income. A Kinh household was also more likely to diverse its income sources to nonagricultural activities.

Generally, the results show that households with better human capital usually have better access to markets. They are, therefore, not only able to have more profitable crops and livestocks but also more able to shift their income portfolio to nonagriculture sources. In addition, households in TTH and DL have more opportunities to switch to nonfarming income sources owing to the better performance of the economy in the two provinces as compared with HT. Moreover, DL households particularly have advantages in growing high-value crops, such as coffee, pepper, and cashew, because of the weather and soil condition.

Trends in Poverty and Inequality

The overall poverty headcount ratio in Vietnam (as measured by per capita expenditure) continued to decrease from closed to 16 percent in 2006 to 14.5 percent in 2008 (GSO 2011). The poverty headcount ratios in the three provinces (as measured by equivalence scaled income) were lower than the ratios (as measured by per capita expenditure) found by Le, Nguyen, and Singh (LNS) (2014) (see Table 2). The three provinces not only made good progress in poverty reduction, but were also successful in keeping the equity of the development as well. The gap between the first and the fifth income quintiles increased slightly from 4.8 to 4.8 and 5.2 over the years, respectively, and the Gini index also increased only marginally from 0.301 to 0.301 and 0.315 over the period.

Table 2 Poverty headcount ratio at national poverty line by province, percent

	Estimated from Vulnerability Surveys			Estimated by LNS	
	2007	2008	2010	2006	2008
Hà Tĩnh	24.8	21.9	16.7	26	29
Thừa Thiên Huế	16.1	11.7	10.6	14	13
Đắk Lắk	19.0	16.4	14.4	17	22
Total	20.6	17.5	14.4	15.9	14.5

Source: Author's calculations from vulnerability surveys in Vietnam and Le, Nguyen, and Singh (LNS) (2014).

The Patterns of Poverty Transitions Across Groups

Over the three-year period, the majority of households stayed nonpoor (slightly over 62 percent) and the other 38 percent was vulnerable to poverty at some level. This pattern shows good progress in poverty reduction in which a large share of the population rose up, approximately 15 percent, and a small share of the population fell down at slightly more than 9 percent. Additionally, a tenth of the population moved around the poverty line (closed to 11 percent) and only a small share stayed poor in all periods (2.3 percent) (see Table 3). The changes in poverty statuses differ across the subgroups of the population. Poverty is usually associated with a large-sized family and a higher burden of dependency. Nonpoor households tend to have fewer members and a lower dependency ratio, 4.1 and 0.4 respectively, while those who are poor in at least one period have nearly five members and a higher dependency ratio of 0.5. In fact,

the poor have low incomes and low asset levels so they tend to live together and share their limited resources (see Table 3).

There is a tendency that young and old households, headed by young or old persons, are more vulnerable to poverty than middle-aged ones. They are less likely to stay nonpoor and are more likely to fall into poverty, fluctuate around the poverty line, or stay poor. Young households are usually newly formed ones, which mean that they also have to invest in bearing and caring for children. Older households are usually wealthier because they have experience in agriculture and livestock production and have accumulated more savings and assets. However, older heads are associated with having lower skills and being less healthy subsequently making them more vulnerable to poverty, which is confirmed by the result of a *t* test.

The education attainment of a household's head tends to have a negative relationship with the vulnerability to poverty. Slightly higher than 56 percent

Table 3 Household and head characteristics by poverty trajectory, percent

	Nonpoor	Rising	Falling	Churning	Poor	Population share
Total	62.4	15.3	9.2	10.8	2.3	100
Household size	4.1	4.9	4.2	4.7	5.1	
Dependency ratio	0.4	0.5	0.5	0.5	0.6	
Head is less than 36 years old	52.6	17.2	9.5	18.1	2.5	17.1
Head is 36–50 years old	70.3	12.3	8.7	8.0	0.7	45.4
Head is 51–65 years old	63.5	15.3	8.4	11.2	1.7	23.9
Head is 66 years and beyond	46.0	23.4	12.1	10.1	8.4	13.6
Head has no schooling	43.9	22.0	12.1	17.0	5.0	13.4
Head attains primary school	54.0	18.6	11.4	11.9	4.1	22.9
Middle school and beyond	69.2	12.8	7.8	9.1	1.1	63.8
Ethnic minority groups	51.5	19.4	10.5	15.9	2.6	15.8
Kinh (majority)	64.4	14.5	9.0	9.9	2.2	84.2
Asset index	0.54	0.39	0.42	0.38	0.24	
Lowlands	65.8	13.2	8.5	10.3	2.3	48.2
Mountainous and highlands	59.1	17.4	9.9	11.3	2.3	51.8
Hà Tĩnh	58.1	17.2	9.1	11.7	4.0	38.6
Thừa Thiên Huế	71.2	12.7	7.2	7.4	1.5	22.2
Đắk Lắk	61.5	15.0	10.4	11.9	1.1	39.2

Notes: Population shares of the same category sum to 100.
Source: Author's calculations from Vulnerability Surveys.

of households headed by men or women without any school are vulnerable to poverty. The share of vulnerable households decreases to 46 percent and 31 percent across the higher education attainment of the head. In addition, only 10 percent of the heads who are from the Kinh are illiterate, while 32 percent of the other heads cannot read or write. Moreover, the Kinh usually live in lowlands, which enables them to have better access to markets and allows them to have a lower risk of being poor.

The asset index is also believed to be a good proxy for household wealth (see Filmer and Pritchett 2001). It differs significantly across population subgroups; nonpoor households are again owners of higher asset levels, while stay-poor households are the least, being 0.54 and 0.24,[4] respectively. In addition, the location of the household can be used as a proxy for public physical asset such as infrastructure and some regional differences. More than half of the households are in mountainous and highland areas where infrastructure such as roads, electricity, schools, and health clinics are in poorer condition and, thus, result in worse market access. Among the chronically poor households, the majority of them are in the mountainous areas in HT where infrastructure is usually of poor conditions, the natural condition is hard for agricultural production, and people are usually from ethnic minority groups who have less access to markets.

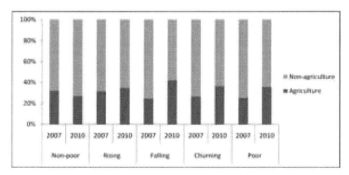

Figure 1 Changes in the patterns of income sources by poverty trajectory, percent

Source: Author's calculations from Vulnerability Surveys.
Notes: Agriculture refers to income from agricultural activities; nonagricultural refers to income from nonagricultural activities.

---

[4] The asset index is scaled to the range of [0,1]

Finally, yet importantly, the patterns of and the changes in income sources also differ across population subgroups. On average, a nonpoor household had an income level of closed to VND 35 million by 2007 and it rose to slightly higher than VND 40 million by 2010. However, its income from agricultural activities stayed at almost the same level of VND 11 million over the same period making a decrease in the share of agricultural activities in the total income. Apparently, households of other groups had a lower income level than the nonpoor ones. By 2007, the incomes of a rising household, a falling one, a churning one, and a poor one were VND 15 million, VND 15 million, VND 14 million, and VND 11 million, respectively. The share of income from agricultural activities to the total household income of household in these groups are significantly higher than this share for nonpoor households, and interestingly the share for the former ones rose over the period, which implies that income from nonagricultural activities of these households increased slower than income from agricultural activities. This was the result of the economic recession in Vietnam started late 2008, causing loss in job, wage cut, etc. and hence affects negatively on remittance, and income from off-farm employment.

Drivers of Poverty Transitions

The marginal effects from the MLN regression show that the increase in the share of income from nonagricultural activities to total household income has an effect on the transitions of poverty. It had a positive relationship with the probability of rising out of poverty,

negative relationship with the probability of falling into poverty as well as with the probability of staying poor (see Table 4). These relationships imply that the transitions toward nonagricultural income sources are good for the household's well-being. Yet, not all the marginal effects are of high levels of significance because the diversity of income sources is not always successful.

Households in Vietnam have a tendency to have smaller sizes owing to the lower birth rate, the increasing migration, and the inclination of living in two generation households. Nevertheless, poor households usually have a larger size because they have more children, less chances to migrate, and having limited resources that prevent them from separating into smaller households. The marginal effects show that households of a larger size and higher dependency ratio have a lower probability of staying nonpoor and a higher probability of being poor in at least one period (see Table 4).

Female-headed households are typically home to more members than male-headed households, and the formers usually have less bread winners than the later, which consequently makes them have higher levels of vulnerability to poverty than their counterparts. In addition, there was no evidence of the difference between the vulnerability to poverty across household sungroups as classified by the head's age. In fact, the poverty dynamics are determined more by the change in the household's livelihood rather than the characteristics of the head (Carter and Barrett 2006), and findings from previous studies do not show the importance of the head's age (Kedir and McKay 2005; Bhide and

Table 4 Marginal effects from multinomial logit model

	Nonpoor	Rising	Falling	Churning	Poor
Increase in the share of nonagriculture income 2007–2008	−0.04701	0.0651***	−0.00744	−0.0102	−0.0011*
	(0.0295)	(0.0175)	(0.0167)	(0.0158)	(0.000820)
Increase in the share of nonagriculture income 2008–2010	−0.00405	0.0597***	−0.0489***	−0.00448	−0.0013**
	(0.0364)	(0.0224)	(0.0197)	(0.0189)	(0.000945)
Household size	−0.0641***	0.0246***	0.0176***	0.0203***	0.00157**
	(0.00993)	(0.00610)	(0.00563)	(0.00542)	(0.000802)
Head is male	0.0808**	−0.00145	−0.0418**	−0.0369*	−0.000644
	(0.0334)	(0.0176)	(0.0207)	(0.0191)	(0.000925)
Head age	−0.000367	0.000721	0.000273	−0.000629	2.54e-06
	(0.000771)	(0.000456)	(0.000425)	(0.000394)	(1.84e-05)
Head is from the Kinh	0.0916***	−0.0486**	−0.0148	−0.0249	−0.00323
	(0.0350)	(0.0238)	(0.0186)	(0.0185)	(0.00252)
Attains primary school	−0.0517	0.0104	0.0347	0.00624	0.000336
	(0.0368)	(0.0199)	(0.0239)	(0.0161)	(0.000776)
Attains middle school and beyond	0.0320	−0.0149	0.00751	−0.0234	−0.00125
	(0.0347)	(0.0205)	(0.0189)	(0.0179)	(0.00111)
Asset index	0.125***	0.345***	−0.192***	−0.265***	−0.0135*
	(0.0729)	(0.0446)	(0.0391)	(0.0376)	(0.00691)
Hà Tĩnh	0.0292	−0.0100	−0.0228	−0.000417	0.00409
	(0.0300)	(0.0195)	(0.0149)	(0.0164)	(0.00304)
Thừa Thiên Huế	−0.0184	0.0334*	−0.0270**	0.00836	0.00366
	(0.0277)	(0.0185)	(0.0131)	(0.0143)	(0.00260)

Notes: Omitted categories: head is female, is from ethnic minority groups, has no schooling, Đắk Lắk, poverty dynamics are referred to national poverty line. All control variables refer to the base year level (2007). Nonagriculture income refers to nonagricultural income. Pseudo R_2 = 0.226, Observations= 1,858. The MNL regression passes tests of IIA assumption. Standard errors in parentheses.
*** $p < 0.01$, ** $p < 0.05$, * $p < 0.1$.

Mehta 2005). In addition, the education attainment of the household head does not contribute to the differences in the probability of being in one or another poverty trajectory. In fact, the more the head is educated, the better his/her access to production resources, labour, and output markets is, and the more efficient he/she is in managing household resources. However, this type of human capital is more likely to have a long-term effect on a household's well-being rather than on the change in shorter period of time.

As discussed earlier, the Kinh are usually more able to access to market and, hence, take advantage of public service and the development process, which allows them to have a higher probability of being nonpoor, and lower probabilities of being poor in one or more periods than their households of ethnic minority groups (see Table 4).

Household wealth as measured by the asset index shows quite strong effects on poverty dynamics. It prevents households from being poor and is negatively correlated with falling into poverty, churning around poverty line, or being poor. It is also positively correlated with staying nonpoor and rising out of poverty (see Table 4). These findings are in line with the discussion of the role of assets in the poverty transitions (Carter and Barrett 2006) as well as with empirical findings from Bhide and Mehta (2005), and Imai, Gaiha, and Kang (2011).

There was little evidence of the difference among households in the three provinces in the vulnerability to poverty. TTH is more dynamic in terms of economic activities owing to the development of the tourism sector,

and the convenience of transportation. Therefore, households in the province have a higher probability of moving out of poverty and a lower probability of falling into poverty than their counterparts in the other two provinces (see Table 4).

Robustness Check

In order to check the robustness of the MNL model for poverty dynamics, the study applies to the transitions of poverty as referred to the poverty line of $2.5 a day (see Table A.2). The MNL regression, the results of which are shown in Table 4, and Table A.2 pass the Hausman tests or suest tests of independence of irrelevant alternatives (IIA), which means that assumptions of IIA could not be rejected; hence, estimates from MNL models are efficient. The reference model, in general, shows similar effects to those in the basic one. However, there are differences in the size of the effects in these models compared to the basic model because poverty dynamics in the additional model refer to a higher poverty line. Additionally, the results from Table 4 are in line with those from previous studies. The results from the MNL regression in this study are, therefore, realizable.

Conclusion

This study uses panel data on households from regions in Vietnam and a multinomial logit model to estimate drivers of poverty transitions. The results show a large share of the population is vulnerable to poverty where 38 percent of households have a risk of being either transient or chronically poor. This risk varies substantially across household groups; households of a large size, ethnic minority groups, and has limited physical assets have a higher risk of being poor since they typically have less access to markets than the other groups, which consequently prevents them from greatly benefiting from the economic growth. These findings are in line with most previous studies by Carter and May (1999), Glewwe, Gragnolati, and Zaman (2000), and Woolard and Klasen (2005).

A household with better access to production inputs and markets is more able to diversify its income sources to nonagricultural activities. The transition toward nonagricultural income sources usually results in higher income and, therefore, an improvement in a household's well being. Particularly, the diversity to nonagricultural income sources is helpful for lifting a household out of poverty, but it is not very helpful for those who churn around the poverty line and the chronically poor. Additionally, nonagricultural activities are subject to shocks and risks, particularly from macroeconomic conditions and market performance. This implies that household developing countries still face challenges in the early stages of income diversity.

Acknowledgements

The author would like to thank anonymous referees and the editor of this journal, and participants at a workshop in Bangkok, particularly Peter Timmer and Jikun Huang, for helpful comments on earlier versions of this paper. Funding from the German Research Foundation (DFG) for supporting the household surveys is gratefully acknowledged.

References

Bhide, Shashanka, and Aasha K. Mehta. 2005. "Tracking Poverty Through Panel Data: Rural Poverty in India 1970–1998." CPRC Working Paper 28. Chronic Poverty Research Centre, University of Manchester.

Cappellari, Lorenzo, and Stephen P. Jenkins. 2004. "Modeling Low Income Transitions." *Journal of Applied Econometrics* 19: 593–610. doi: 10.1002/jae.778.

Carter, Michael R., and Christopher B. Barrett. 2006. "The Economics of Poverty Traps and Persistent Poverty: An Asset-Based Approach." *Journal of Development Studies* 42: 178–199. doi: 10.1080/00220380500405261.

Carter, Michael R., and Julian May. 1999. "Poverty, Livelihood and Class in Rural South Africa." *World Development* 27: 1–20. doi: 10.1016/S0305-750X(98)001 29-6.

De Janvry, A., M. Fafchamps, and E. Sadoulet. 1991. "Peasant Household Behavior with Missing Markets: Some Paradoxes Explained." *Economic Journal* 101: 1400–1417.

Filmer, Deon, and Lant H. Pritchett. 2001. "Estimating Wealth Effects Without Expenditure Data—or Tears: An Application to Educational Enrollments in States of India." *Demography* 38: 115–132.

General Statistics Office (GSO). 2011. *Result of the Vietnam Living Standard Survey 2010*. Hanoi: Statistical Publishing House.

Glewwe, Paul, Michele Gragnolati, and Hassan Zaman. 2000. "Who Gained from Vietnam's Boom in the 1990s?." Policy Research Working Paper 2275, The World Bank.

Imai, Katsushi S., Raghav Gaiha, and Woojin Kang. 2011. "Vulnerability and Poverty Dynamics in Vietnam." *Applied Economics* 43: 3603–3618. doi: 10.1080/00036841003670754.

Justino, Patricia, Julie Litchfield, and Hung Thai Pham. 2008. "Poverty Dynamics during Trade Reform Evidence from Rural Vietnam." *Review of Income and Wealth* 54: 166–192. doi: 10.1111/j.1475-4991.2008.00269.x.

Kedir, Abbi M., and Andrew McKay. 2005. "Chronic Poverty in Urban Ethiopia: Panel Data Evidence." *International Planning Studies* 10: 49–67. doi: 10.1080/13563470500159246.

Kinsey, B., K. Burger, and J.W. Gunning. 1998. "Coping with Drought in Zimbabwe: Survey Evidence on Responses of Rural Households to Risks." *World Development* 26 (1): 89–110.

Klasen, Stephan, and Hermann Waibel, eds. 2012. *Vulnerability to Poverty: Theory, Measurement and Determinants, with Case Studies from Thailand and Vietnam*. Basingstoke: Palgrave Macmillan.

Le, M. Son, Duc Tho Nguyen, and Tarlok Singh. 2014. "Economic Growth and Poverty in Vietnam: Evidence from Elasticity Approach." Discussion Paper 2014-01, Griffith Business School.

McCulloch, Neil, and Bob Baulch. 1999. "Dishtinguishing the Chronically from the Transitory Poor: Evidence from Pakistan." IDS Working Paper 97. Institute of Development Studies, University of Sussex.

Organisation for Economic Co-operation and Development (OECD). 1982. *The OECD List of Social Indicators*. Paris: Organisation for Economic Co-operation and Development.

Tran, Q. Van, Sabina Alkire, and Stephan Klasen. 2015. "Static and Dynamic Disparities between Monetary and Multidimensional Poverty Measurement: Evidence from Vietnam." *Research on Economic Inequality* 23: 249–281. 10.1108/S1049-258520150000023008.

Woolard, Ingrid, and Stephan Klasen. 2005. "Determinants of Income Mobility and Household Poverty Dynamics in South Africa." *The Journal of Development Studies* 41: 865–897.

Wooldridge, Jeffrey M. 2002. *Econometric Analysis of Cross Section and Panel Data*. London: The MIT Press.

World Bank. 2013, January. Data: Indicators. http://data.worldbank.org/indicator.

Appendix

Table A.1 Components of asset index and their weights

Assets	Eigenvalue	Proportion
Household has a motobike	3.42	0.24
Household has a television	1.36	0.10
Household has an electric rice cooker	1.13	0.08
Household has a mattress	1.05	0.07
Household has a video player	0.96	0.07
Household cooks with electricity/gas	0.89	0.06
Household uses improved sanitation facility	0.81	0.06
Household has an electric fan	0.76	0.05
Household has a fridge	0.68	0.05
Household has improved flooring	0.64	0.05
House size	0.63	0.05
House (wall and roof) is made of improved materials	0.61	0.04
Household has radio	0.55	0.04
Household has a bike	0.52	0.04

Note: Proportions sum to one.

Table A.2 Marginal effects from MNL for poverty dynamics as referred to $2.5

	Nonpoor	Rising	Falling	Churning	Poor
Increase in the share of nonagricultural income 2007-2008	-0.0240	0.0218	-0.0285	0.00956	0.00775
	(0.0418)	(0.0281)	(0.0241)	(0.0250)	(0.00631)
Increase in the share of nonagricultural income 2008-2010	-0.0556	0.0792**	0.0595**	-0.0358	-0.0424
	(0.0529)	(0.0353)	(0.0296)	(0.0311)	(0.00741)
Household size	0.0842***	-0.0393***	-0.0157**	-0.0154*	-0.0137***
	(0.0137)	(0.00933)	(0.00798)	(0.00846)	(0.00303)
Head is male	0.0306	0.0544**	-0.0440	-0.0253	-0.0158*
	(0.0439)	(0.0245)	(0.0276)	(0.0273)	(0.00823)
Head age	-0.00241**	0.00260***	0.00102	-0.00136**	0.000165
	(0.00116)	(0.000734)	(0.000644)	(0.000685)	(0.000152)
Head is from the Kinh	0.187***	-0.111***	-0.0146	-0.0121	-0.0492***
	(0.0434)	(0.0359)	(0.0257)	(0.0264)	(0.0175)
Attains primary school	0.0319	0.00382	-0.00671	-0.0322	0.00320
	(0.0520)	(0.0327)	(0.0274)	(0.0249)	(0.00649)
Attains middle school and beyond	0.124**	-0.0358	-0.0148	-0.0641**	-0.00954
	(0.0516)	(0.0338)	(0.0286)	(0.0309)	(0.00735)
Asset index	0.509***	0.495***	-0.355***	-0.452***	-0.150***
	(0.113)	(0.0719)	(0.0592)	(0.0617)	(0.0273)
Hà Tĩnh	-0.0611	0.0112	-0.0316	0.0355	0.0460***
	(0.0415)	(0.0296)	(0.0216)	(0.0270)	(0.0149)
Thừa Thiên Huế	0.0873**	-0.0173	-0.0685***	-0.0104	0.00901
	(0.0378)	(0.0254)	(0.0190)	(0.0229)	(0.00741)

Notes: Omitted categories: head is female, head is from ethnic minority groups, head has no schooling, Đắk Lắk, poverty dynamics are referred to national poverty line. All control variables refer to the base year level (2007). Pseudo $R_2 = 0.257$, Observations= 1,858. The MNL regression passes tests of IIA assumption. Standard errors in parentheses. *** $p<0.01$, ** $p<0.05$, * $p<0.1$

The World Food Economy:
A 40 Year Perspective on the Past, and a Look Forward

C. Peter Timmer[A]

What has changed in the world food economy in the 40 years since 1975? The basic answer to that question is that ending hunger has turned out to be a very difficult task. Henry Kissinger stated in 1976, at the first World Food Conference, that "within a decade, no child will go to bed hungry." There would be no hunger within a decade. We failed miserably in that promise and the question then is why? This paper attempts to answer that question.

There are two basic questions: (1) What has changed, and what has remained the same? (2) Why is ending hunger so hard? What has changed, obviously, is an information and communications technological revolution that has radically reduced the transactions costs of doing business. Even poor households can be informed instantly about market prices. What has remained the same is that resource scarcity continues as the dominant theme organizing market activities. Making markets work for the poor is the only path out of hunger and poverty.

Keywords: Food security, markets, ICT revolution, world food economy, ending hunger

Introduction

What is the special significance of a 40 year perspective, from the vantage point of 2015? The answer is mostly personal. In 1975, I first taught a course at Stanford University on the world food economy. It was a course that had a long history at the Stanford Food Research Institute, which had been founded in 1921. Merrill Bennett first taught the course, starting in the 1950s.[1] After Bennett's retirement in 1960, Bruce Johnston took over the course and gave it more of an Asian and African focus. But Bruce was on sabbatical in Kenya in 1975 and I was asked if I would step in as a young faculty and teach a course on the world food economy.

[A] This is a lightly edited version of the Keynote Speech I delivered at the World Food Policy Conference, December 17–18, 2015 in Bangkok, Thailand. The Conference was sponsored by the Thai Royal Society. I am the Cabot Professor of Development Studies, *emeritus*, Harvard University, and Non-Resident Fellow, Center for Global Development, Washington, DC. Fuller details are available in my book, *Food Security and Scarcity: Why Ending Hunger Is So Hard* (Philadelphia, PA: University of Pennsylvania Press) 2015.

[1] Bennett's well-known book, *The World Food Economy* (New York: Harper and Row), was published in 1954 and was an outgrowth of teaching the course.

doi: 10.18278/wfp.2.2.3.1.8

That is the starting point of what I consider my own serious deliberation, serious thinking, and serious analysis of how the world food economy works and what goes wrong with it. Some of us in the room are old enough to remember that in 1975 we were just winding down from a very serious world food crisis. It started with rice in Asia in late 1972—and spread very quickly to maize and wheat right around the world. And the world food crisis corresponded also with an energy crisis, the formation of OPEC, and restriction of oil supplies because of the Yom Kippur war. The commodity boom that we witnessed in the mid-1970s really changed how people in the world were thinking—not just about whether food was going to be available—but the linkages between energy and food going forward.

So, the question is what has changed in those 40 years? The bottom line answer to that question will be a conclusion that ending hunger has turned out to be a very difficult task. Some of us remember Henry Kissinger stating in 1976, at the first World Food Conference, that "within a decade, no child will go to bed hungry." No one would have to worry about having enough food on the table. There would be no hunger within a decade. We failed miserably in that promise and the question then is why? That is my topic today.

The Quest for Food Security since 1975

There are two basic questions:

- What has changed, and what has remained the same?
- Why is ending hunger so hard?

Let me take them in turn, starting with some personal landmarks. First is a two-volume issue of *Food Research Institute Studies* published in 1975 on the "Political Economy of Rice in Asia." I did the methodological introduction, the chapter on Indonesia, and the conclusions for that volume. Professor Ammar Siamwalla did the chapter on Thailand.

A book titled *Food Policy Analysis* that Wally Falcon and Scott Pearson and I wrote was published in 1983.[2] Amazingly it is still used in courses on the world food economy and on food policy—even though it is >30 years old and is dated in rather serious ways. On the other hand, the book laid out a framework for thinking about food issues in the context of trade, macroeconomics, and household decision making, while integrating all those components. The 1983 book was really the first time we were able to pull all this together for the profession.

In 1988, I published a chapter in the *Handbook of Development Economics* on the "Agricultural Transformation."[3] That

---

[2] C. Peter Timmer, Walter P. Falcon and Scott R. Pearson, *Food Policy Analysis* (Baltimore, MD: Johns Hopkins University Press for the World Bank, 1983).

[3] C. Peter Timmer. "The Agricultural Transformation," in *Handbook of Development Economics*, vol. 1, eds. Hollis Chenery, and T.N. Srinivasan (Amsterdam, North-Holland: Elsevier, 1988), 275–331.

chapter came out of a growing sense that we did not understand what was happening in terms of agricultural development, and how agricultural productivity fed out into national economies and then to the world food economy. We could not understand that process without understanding what happens to agriculture during modern economic growth and equally important, what is the role of agriculture in stimulating that economic growth. This is a two-way relationship and we have to think about both directions—you can't do just one or the other. Both of them are important.

And then in 2009, I published a little monograph for the American Enterprise Institute (AEI) called "A world without agriculture: The structural transformation in historical perspective." Based on my Wendt Lecture at AEI, this volume looked at the endpoint of the economic growth process in terms of where agriculture fits in rich countries. And the simple answer is there are more lawyers in the United States than there are farmers. There are more dry-cleaning establishments in the United States than there are farm establishments. If you want to think about the share of agriculture in the economy as it goes to a very small proportion, in rich countries agriculture is <1% or 2% of both the work force and its contribution to GDP. But in all rich countries agriculture is *more productive, producing more output than it ever did*. It seems like a paradox, that the success of

agriculture and expanding output ends up making it less important to policy and to the economy.

I come to the conclusion today, after studying this whole historical process, and from being involved for over 40 years in the field of agricultural development, with the second question I raised: Why is ending hunger so hard?

That is our agenda after all. Basically, what we are trying to do if we are interested in food and agriculture—we are trying to figure out a way to reduce poverty and to end hunger. Everything else is a means to that end. The world community just committed itself at the Sustainable Development Goals Meeting in October 2015, at the UN in New York to ending poverty and hunger in the next 15 years—to do it by 2030. So, the question is why didn't similar pledges over the last 40 or 50 years resulted in that outcome—and what are the chances of actually making that promise come true?

There happens to be a book on that topic that just came out this year (2015): "Food Security and Scarcity: Why Ending Hunger Is So Hard?"[4]

---

[4] C. Peter Timmer, *Food Security and Hunger: Why Ending Hunger Is So Hard* (Philadelphia, PA: University of Pennsylvania Press, 2015).

The book focuses on four main themes:

First is the complex role of markets. This is not the place to debate the role of capitalism as a system to organize our economic affairs. That debate is taking place in all rich countries, mostly because of the extreme inequalities in incomes generated by the financialization of capitalism. My concern is both narrower and broader. I want to focus on the *role of markets* in the economy because we may have to distinguish between the institutional framework in which these markets are set (and the regulations that market participants face) and the role that the markets themselves have to play.

Second is the importance of government policies. I learned about development when I first went to Indonesia, my Ph.D. still hot in my hand, in 1970. My first appointment was as a junior advisor for the Harvard Advisory Group in the National Planning Agency. I had never taken a course in development. I am an economic historian by training, but I had analyzed commodity markets for 2 years on Wall Street. I certainly had a sense of how commodity markets work—I used to spend my lunch break watching the floor trading at the New York Coffee and Sugar Exchange. At the time, of course, Indonesia was a major commodity exporter. So there was a need for some expertise on how world markets work for the things that Indonesia exported (and the Indonesian government reluctantly agreed, because of my inexperience in developing countries) to let me serve as a Harvard advisor on these commodities. But I was explicitly not supposed to work on food commodities.

You cannot sit in a national planning agency and think that government policy is irrelevant, even if the technical terms of reference are to study the behavior of world commodity markets. That is simply not the mindset. I was there for almost 2 years and then back two to three times a year for the next 40 years. For better or worse, I am conditioned to think it is important that the government do the right thing. That is the role of food policy analysis, and the role of government is really very important in this. Markets may do a lot of the work but governments have to intervene as well. But how, to do what?

Third is the historical process of structural transformation. This has been in some sense my major academic role. I was Professor at Harvard for many years, Stanford and Cornell before that. I tried to understand this whole historical process of structural transformation—and especially the role of agriculture. I am a product of Alexander Gerschenkron, who lectured on economic backwardness in historical perspective. He thought agriculture was part of the problem in the development process. It was backward, it had people who weren't educated—you couldn't get them into the factories to work on time. Agriculture was the problem and industrialization—the faster the better—was the solution to modernization. His work focused almost entirely on the European experience. I was molded by that introduction to the historical process of thinking about the problems that come up during the development process. "Constraints" were simply opportunities for substituting other ways of solving a problem—not as barriers that meant a constraint that prevented doing anything. The European experience was seeing the constraint, then doing it some other way than the British did it—the Germans will do it differently than the French did it—but it's still attacking the same basic structural transformation.

The need to identify the appropriate time horizon for analysis and interventions. With all due respect to our opening speaker—to the Deputy Prime Minister—I think we all understand that it is extremely difficult to get policymakers and politicians to focus on anything other than the short-run realities that they are coping with. Five years out is an eternity. Fifty years out might as well be of zero interest—you can't even begin to think about that.

This long-term historical perspective is best illustrated by a picture of the structural transformation in Japan and Indonesia—starting in 1880 and going to 2010—a 130 years of economic development and structural transformation and they aren't done yet. Again, with all due respect, I think, policymakers need to have this strategic framework in their head and in front of their analysts.

These four themes are not new, but integrating them into a coherent approach to ending hunger seems to be original and is the contribution of the book. But it is the *integration* of these

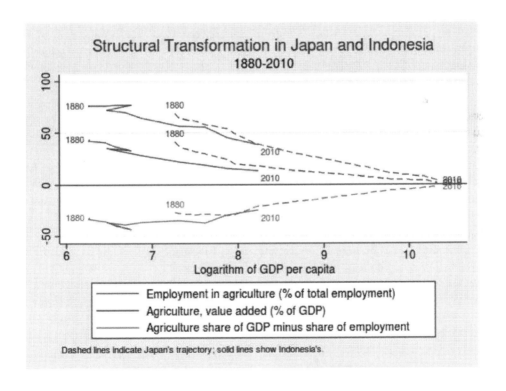

Structural Transformation in Japan and Indonesia
1880-2010

Dashed lines indicate Japan's trajectory; solid lines show Indonesia's.

four themes, which is really hard. It is conceptually difficult, it is operationally difficult, and we all understand that it is politically difficult. Here, I won't try to speak on the realities of policymaking in Thailand. But I can tell you that in Indonesia we have a very difficult time getting the parliament to deal with anything other than the extremely short run. In the United States we don't take policy seriously any longer at all. The disconnect from what I would call "reality" in the US political scene is just astonishing. So, this is going to be hard because it's going to require we get policy right. It's going to require that we do the analysis and inform policy choices.

The rich countries are lucky because they have enough resources that they can do this—keep people from starving—even if things are not completely right. There is plenty of slack in the economy so that the poor need not starve—that is just a programmatic issue and it is not a policy or a development issue. Rich countries have largely managed this integration, and ended widespread hunger, because they have abundant resources for the tasks. But for poor countries, they have had to manage hunger while they were still poor. Only a few poor countries have managed to end hunger while they were relatively poor, and most of them are here in Southeast Asia and China. The lessons from those success stories in this region drive the analysis of the book.

Why is ending hunger so hard?

Ending hunger is hard because it is a lengthy process that requires sustained policy attention and public resources, and also at the same time private markets are the main arena for nearly all the decisions that matter: public policy, private markets. The food system is at the core of this process in both the long run and short run. In the long run, the food system is a key element of the structural transformation, which historically has been the only sustainable pathway out of poverty. In the short run, the food system is where many of the poor make their living and also face the risks of volatile food prices.

Structural transformation has been the only sustainable pathway out of poverty—you have to get people from very tiny farms with low productivity jobs to better jobs—often in rural areas but sometimes in the urban economy. The structural transformation changes the relationship of the labor force in the economy between agriculture and the rest, especially in urban areas. The structural transformation has been the only successful pathway out of poverty and where it has not worked we have not been able to end poverty. Being a small farmer is a very risky undertaking in an environment of endemic poverty.

Main Message: The "Wicked Problem"

Australians coined the term "wicked problem" to describe climate change, because it is so complicated that no single individual, no single discipline, no single school, and no single think tank can figure it out. It's just much too complicated—that's what a wicked problem is. Now, there is a growing acceptance that food security is a wicked problem, it is a very complex thing to pull off.

First of all, to solve the problem of food insecurity, markets have to do the "heavy lifting"—markets have to be the arena where virtually every decision that matters is going to get made. There are three things markets have to do. There are engineering functions: they have to move inputs and outputs from the farm through the processing sector into retail—moving and transforming the product in time, in place, and form. Whether the Soviet Union or North Korea—any kind of socialist, planned economy—they still have to do this. I was in China in 1975 there was total denial by the Maoists at the time that markets did anything. But China moved its grain, its vegetables, and its livestock products in time, place, and form—they transformed them. They actually had to do all of these functions. *Now the question is how do you do them efficiently?* That was not a question that the Chinese were asking from the point of view of an economist, they were asking from the point of view of an engineer—a planner in that sense. But if you do these tasks efficiently—transportation, storage, processing—the marketing sector becomes the arena for price discovery because the different *prices* at each stage in the marketing chain have to match the *costs* of creating the value added: milling the rice, moving from farm gate to warehouse, or storing it from the harvest season to the short season. Each of those costs involves real economic resources and what we want for efficiency is the costs of doing those tasks gets matched by the price differentials so that the people

who will do these marketing activities sort of automatically know that they can make a little profit if they can move rice from West Java to Jakarta, for example.

So the marketing system then becomes the locus for price discovery and for efficient exchange of commodities. Each time a transaction happens, these commodities typically change hands— they get a new owner. Increasingly, with modern supply chains and supermarkets at the end, there may be a single ownership pattern all the way back to the farm. Typically, of course, farmers are usually not part of that process. In more traditional marketing systems, the commodities change hands—there has to be an agreement on the terms of the exchange. All of this sounds very busy. There must be 10 billion or more of those transactions every single day. Planning agencies can't plan that. You need to get the price discovery and the efficient exchange working almost automatically so that governments don't have to do this, the market does it. The critical role for the market is this discovery of prices that leads to efficient exchange. And when those prices are out and visible—transparent if you like—then they provide signals to producers and to consumers for efficient resource allocation. If the price is high, you want farmers to be investing more in increasing output. You want consumers to look for substitutes for rice—be it cassava or corn (or eggs or pork).

That's what responding to these price signals is all about. And when those responses are reasonably flexible you get efficient resource allocation. It is simply impossible to sustain poverty reduction without using our resources reasonably efficiently. I am not a Chicago economist that insists that this all works perfectly. But we have to make these markets work pretty well because we need those billions of transactions done every day automatically and they've got to point the economy in the right direction instead of the wrong direction.

Once markets are working pretty well, governments have to do the right things and they have to stop doing the wrong things. The problem is of course: What's right? What's wrong? If I had really been trained in Chicago (instead of Harvard), I might have been able to give a fairly simple answer to that—markets work perfectly all the time. But I wasn't. What's right and what's wrong varies by country, by stages of development, it changes over time—and it requires continuous policy analysis—and it requires pretty significant flexibility on the part of policymakers. We have heard about knowledge-based learning in the policy process. That's exactly what we have to have. Because, as circumstances change policies will have to change and you have to know what's going on in order to bring informed analysis to the debate.

The bottom line, unfortunately, is that the political economy of this is really tricky. That is because we need policymakers to understand what's going on in the markets and when things are going bad for income distribution, economic growth, and stability—all of which the market doesn't really care about, but citizens do. When those market outcomes are not working on behalf of the welfare of citizens, governments need to do the "right thing" and not the "wrong thing." The analytics of determining what to do are difficult, but the political economy of doing it is really, really difficult.

Defining Food Security: 3 Pillars and 2 Platforms

I think of food policy as having three basic pillars—columns if you like—and those pillars sit on one base and also have a top, so there are two platforms. The pillars now are well received in the food security literature and debates—availability, access, and utilization.

You cannot have food security unless the food is available. So, availability is one of the pillars, perhaps even the first pillar. It depends on food production, plus imports, minus exports—obviously there can also be changes from losses and storage—but the basic point is important. Please understand that the availability pillar is not just food production. Trade is an important component for almost every country in the world in being able to achieve food security. It's very important that we keep that trade option. But it is also true that the earth as a planet is closed. We can't trade with the moon or with Mars. So in a global sense, production really does determine availability. In the very short run we can worry about how large food reserves are. But over the longer run—production is critical—you cannot consume the food unless you produce it.

The second pillar is access to food. It took quite a while—it took really until the food crisis in the 1970s for the profession to really understand that food security is anything more than production and reserves. There was plenty of food in the world. The 1983 book *Food Policy Analysis* starts out by doing the caloric conversion of the major grains and root tubers, the protein crops—it didn't even look at meat—just the calorie and protein conversions, added them up, divided by the world's population—and there was ~30% surplus in terms of any meaningful requirements of humans for nutrient intake. Obviously then, access is at least as important in determining who is food secure and who is not as aggregate availability.

Amartya Sen would call this an "entitlement" mechanism. Indeed, I think this whole access issue sets up a dichotomy between a Malthusian view of the world, where population is going to grow so fast against a fixed resource base that famine would be the mechanism by which we keep our population under control versus a Sen-ian view of the world: there is plenty

of food out there. If we are going to solve the problem of food insecurity we are going to have to figure out ways for households who do not have that access to get it. That can be through public action, it can be by getting them a good job and it can be just a straightforward food distribution scheme from the World Food Program. There are a lot of ways you can think about it, but making sure that poor households have access to food is critical and certainly the recent experience (the last 50 years) has been that we have enough on the availability side and access is the really serious constraint in solving this problem.

- Pillars
    - Availability: food production + imports – exports
    - Access: produce or buy (and Malthus vs Sen)
    - Utilization: sanitation, health, nutrition
- Platforms
    - Stability: both access *and* availability
    - Sustainability
        - Agro-ecological
        - Incomes of the poor

Those three pillars sit on two platforms, one on top and the other on the bottom. Increasingly now the international community that deals with food security understands that stability of this whole food security system is critical. It doesn't work for poor households to have access to food over the average of a year or 5 years if there are spikes and shortages because you pretty much need food every day or on a regular basis. And so stability is a real issue. Most of the profession focuses on the stability at the *availability* side, making sure that droughts and typhoons

don't destroy the food that is necessary to go into the market. But stability of *access* is equally important because things can happen in terms of income or, if you like,—entitlement mechanisms of poor households so that even when the food is in the market, if they lose their job or they lose their ability to access what food there is, then they're simply not food secure.

The other platform is the sustainability of this system, an issue of increasing urgency. Again, there are two dimensions that we should think about: (1) sustainability, as usually thought of as an ecological concern—making sure that we don't mine our agricultural resources, our soils and our water, in a way that in 10 years they're gone and you can't continue to produce. But we also need to think about (2) sustaining the incomes of the poor and the poor often rely heavily on exactly those resources. So, this is going to be a tricky debate going forward.

Three Levels of Food Security

With that complicated definition in place, we need to understand that there are three different levels of food security, each with its own unique (but overlapping) issues.

We *measure* food security at the household level. Ideally, we would always be measuring food security at the individual level because it is the individuals that matter. But the data are often not available for individuals. Instead, usually what we have is: (1) how much food is available in the household and (2) the composition and size of the household. With these data, we do the appropriate adjustments and try to figure out what's going on for the individuals in the household. But this is where we measure food insecurity, it's at the household level.

I think of this as the *micro* level. A lot of the food security community stops at that point and says let's make sure we know what's going on at the household level—see how the trends are changing and understand the characteristics of the households that have enough food and the characteristics of the ones that do not have enough food, end of story, and deal with the problem at that level. The difficulty with that is there is a food security issue that shows up at the national level— what I would call the *macro* side of food security—and it happens to be the food security level that policymakers worry about. They worry about whether urban markets have adequate food supplies at reasonably stable prices—stable food

---

Three levels of food security

- Household level (micro: degree of undernourishment)
- National level (macro: reflected in urban markets as stable prices for staple foodstuffs)
- Global level (international market prices and the race between growth in demand and supply)
- Policy issues different from level to level

prices for the key food stuffs—imagine rice in the major cities of Asia.

Food security for policymakers is actually a pretty clear concept: knowing that those urban markets have adequate supplies and the prices are reasonably stable. Why? Because urban households do not have the option of growing their own food. They have to go to the market and even though they may be reasonably wealthy, if the market supplies disappear—if suddenly there is a scare as there was in 2007 and 2008—if rice suddenly disappears from the shelves in the market—you've got a really serious problem on your hand, *even if there is enough rice out there*. We even had a food scare in California in 2008, people started going to the major supermarkets and buying the rice off the shelf because they were afraid there wasn't going to be rice next week or the week after that and they wanted to be sure they got it. What's the surest thing that will happen if everybody panics? There will not be any rice on the shelves. It's just guaranteed by human nature.

I think it is entirely appropriate for policymakers at the national level to take this issue really seriously. That is partly because history has made it very clear the if you can't keep rice in the market at stable prices you will not be the government going forward, whether it's elected or whether it's military. You can't keep the trust of the people and without the trust of the people you simply cannot govern—it's just as simple as that.

Beyond the micro and macro levels of food security is a third level: the global level. As I said earlier, we can't import or export at a global level (although in principle we could hold food reserves at a global level). At the national level, if you're running low on rice stocks in Indonesia you can come to Thailand and get some rice. But globally if we're running out of rice, reserves all around the world in different countries have been exhausted and there is no place to go. So we have to maintain the production capability at a global level that ensures the supplies we will need at the national level, which then would go down to the household level.

That global level is important. The difficulty, of course, is there is no real mechanism for ensuring global supplies. The Food and Agriculture Organization (FAO) may think that this is their job—but they don't control any budgets in agricultural ministries in any country. These are decisions that have to be made at national levels. They can be helped by the research from the International Rice Research Institute (IRRI) and other research centers. There are global public goods that are out there, trade agreements with the World Trade Organization (WTO)—all of these things can help. But in fact, these key decisions will have to be made at the national level. They need to be informed by what's happening globally and that's the task.

The bottom line here is clear: policy issues are really different from one level to the other and a good food policy analyst needs to understand the different policy issues at each level—but then how are they connected? How do we get from what's going on in the world food economy to the macro and micro levels? How do we get down to national level food security policy debates and then how do we deliver and make sure households have access to the food that they need?

What has driven changes in food security over the past three decades?

There are three big topics that we need to discuss.[5] First is the changing global environment, in which national food systems are set. The global economy is more connected, more competitive, and more driven by the economies of emerging nations. Second is the return of food price volatility. Between 1982 and 2002, food prices kept falling. They were very stable and it looked like you could just forget about food price volatility and scarcity as the driver of any problems. You may have access issues, but you don't have to worry about volatility and supplies. Now, food price volatility is back. The third topic, which has been on my intellectual horizon for many years but which now has entered the policy debate in a serious manner, is the growth in income inequality within very important countries and across countries.[6]

There are many dimensions to the changing global environment, and they can be mentioned only briefly here:

Rapid economic growth, especially in Asia. Because of its speed and the number of households involved, Asia's economic growth has led to the emergence of hundreds of millions of households into the middle class, with new demands—demands for automobiles, television sets, but also demands for improved diets. A dietary transition comes with this rapid economic growth that includes more meat, seafood, and high-quality fruits and vegetables. This dietary transition also comes with significant health consequences.

The ICT revolution. Modern information and communications technology is important at both household and international levels. The ability to communicate almost instantly transforms how efficiently markets can operate because markets operate on information. The faster they can get the information the more efficient they will be. It doesn't have to be in billions of a second the way the US stock market operates, but the fast transmission of information, and its accessibility to all market participants, is very important.

Global financial integration. Global financial markets have become interested in the emerging economies, and this interest is not necessarily all for the good. Yes, having access to cheaper sources of capital so you can build expensive infrastructure is fine. But if the funds are "hot money" and the country is building a road with it, there is a mismatch in the time horizon that gets really scary when the money suddenly flows out. Then you can't meet your bills, you have to depreciate your domestic currency,

---

[5] Even though there was little time to do so in the lecture itself. The topics of food price volatility and impact of income inequality have been treated elsewhere and were not discussed at length in the lecture.

[6] As an example of that early interest, see, for example, "Growth, Inequality and Poverty Alleviation: Implications for Development Assistance" (with M. K. Gugerty). CAER II Discussion Paper (Cambridge, MA: Harvard Institute for International Development, November 1999).

and suddenly you've got a macro crisis on your hands. That financial volatility is not how you get investors in these countries to take the long view they need in order to make these long-term investments in infrastructure, factories, and equipment.

The changing nature of economic growth. Starting in the 1990s, China and a number of other poor countries began a several-decade long spurt of economic growth that changed the nature of demand for basic commodities: metals, coal, and petroleum. The former chairman of the Federal Reserve Board, Alan Greenspan, commented in the mid-1990s, about the "weightless" economic growth that we saw in advanced countries. It didn't use any natural resources. It was all based on new knowledge of the sort produced in Silicon Valley. Although it needs a bit of electricity, basically economic growth was not resource intensive in the rich world. But when economic growth in the world was being driven by China, India, Brazil, Indonesia, and other countries that needed roads, buildings, railways, harbors, airports, cars, and trucks—that takes cement, copper, iron, and steel—it takes real commodities and it takes energy to fuel that whole expansion. So, economic growth is no longer weightless and the emergence of India and China as significant drivers of global economic growth has changed the nature of world commodity markets. It has taken the whole financial community some time to get that all sorted out.

High energy prices. Actually, the issue is high but volatile energy prices, because oil is US$37 per barrel instead of US$137, and the commodity bust being experienced late in 2015 emphasize the importance of price volatility as well as price levels. But high energy prices for well over a decade, especially from 2000 to 2014, was a "game changer" for agriculture. When energy prices are high, it makes economic sense in the marketplace to convert food commodities into liquid fuel: gasoline and diesel fuel. Corn from the American mid-west can be run through an ethanol plant and that ethanol fuels an automobile. If we use the entire corn crop in the United States to make ethanol, it would provide ~15% of our liquid fuel demand for the automobile fleet in the United States. Of relevance to the world food economy, Latin America particularly responded very vigorously to these opportunities in terms of producing sugar-based ethanol, and by producing more corn and soybeans for export as feed for the livestock needed for the dietary transition. But high energy prices mean high food prices because bio-fuels link food commodities to energy markets and that turned out to be very scary. We have some breathing space now. But we need to stop the mandates on bio-fuels, and I would like to see taxes on bio-fuels made from food commodities (rather than the subsidies that exist in many countries). Here is a clear case where the market is not getting it right. We're going to need reforms and sensible tax policy.

Climate change. There is not time for a serious discussion of the impact of climate change on the world food economy, but sharply increased instability in weather seems to be coming—with more droughts and worse flooding, often in the same locations in the same year. This instability will affect agricultural productivity—especially in areas that need productivity growth the most: Sub-Saharan Africa in particular.

Fortunately, my thoughts on how to cope with climate change appeared in the inaugural issue of *World Food Policy*, so I can end with that reference.[7]

---

[7] Peter Timmer, "Coping with Climate Change: A Food Policy Approach," World Food Policy (Inaugural Issue) 1 (1) (Spring 2014): 56–71.

Food Security in an Age of Falling Commodity and Food Prices

Stefan Tangermann[A]

International prices of food and agricultural commodities had reached an extremely high level in 2007-08 and subsequent years, but have more recently embarked on a declining trend. It is, though, not certain that they will reach the lower levels again that prevailed before the price peak. It appears conceivable that international markets have experienced a structural shift towards a longer-term higher price level. While there is no certainty that prices will remain at such a higher level it appears that the international community should at least be prepared for such an outcome. High international food prices can undermine global food security as developing countries overall, and low-income countries in particular, are net importers of food and agricultural products. Their net imports keep growing, above all those of cereals. In many developing countries, even rural households are net buyers of food. An increase in food prices reduces welfare and impacts negatively on food security in net importing countries and among net-buying households. As far as policy implications are concerned, this means that high-price policies, implemented through import tariffs and domestic measures, cannot be recommended for developing countries. The international community needs to invest more in agricultural development and food security in developing countries. We must not repeat he experience of the mid-1970s, when the promises to do more for agricultural development after a similar period of food price peaks were soon forgotten after prices declined again.

Keywords: *International food prices; global trends on food markets; net imports of food in developing countries; welfare implications of changing food prices; policies to improve food security*

In recent years, international markets for commodities and food have gone through exciting if not worrying price swings. The well-known secular decline of prices in real (i.e., inflation corrected) terms and a period of several years of price depression were suddenly interrupted by a dramatic increase of prices in 2007. Food prices, in particular those of cereals and rice, reached a peak in 2008, far above the real prices that had prevailed in the last 20 years or so. In a number of developing countries food security was severely threatened or actually undermined. Several governments around the world responded in panic and adopted measures, both domestically and at the border, aimed at keeping food prices under control. The

[A] Professor Emeritus, Department of Agricultural Economics and Rural Development, University of Göttingen, Göttingen, Germany. Paper presented at the World Food Policy Conference, 17–18 December 2015, Bangkok.

doi: 10.18278/wfp.2.2.3.1.9

international community was deeply concerned about global food security and the world's capacity to feed a growing population. Several high-level meetings were held, all the way up to the ranks of heads of state and government, to consider programs that could improve the state of affairs. And indeed, all sorts of promises were made to assist countries in need, to calm down the situation on international food markets and to foster the productivity of world agriculture.[1]

After their 2008 peak, food prices on international markets as well as prices of other commodities declined again for some time, though by far not to the much lower levels that had prevailed before 2007. But then prices began to rise again, and for a number of years they fluctuated around rather high levels, with an extraordinary degree of volatility. Beginning in 2014, though, commodity and food prices embarked on a declining trend that appears to continue, if not to accelerate, until these days. While the precarious situation of food consumers was a major matter of concern in the years following 2007, the fate of farmers around the world has come into sharp focus as agricultural commodity prices appear to be ever declining. Yet, as many farmers, in particular in developing countries, are also poor food consumers, the pressure that declining farm product prices impose on farm incomes may also have negative implications for their food security. This complex web of relationships between changing market trends and food security was the theme of the presentation to the

Bangkok World Food Policy Conference in December 2015 on which this article is based.

When discussing this theme, three specific questions would appear to be particularly relevant. (1) Is the price decline experienced in the recent past likely to continue? (2) What are the implications for world food security? (3) How should policies, both domestic and international, respond? The article is structured along the lines of these three questions. The focus will be on prices of food and agricultural commodity prices, while other commodities will be mentioned only in passing. Given the limited time available for the presentation, the treatment of the theme dealt with here is necessarily somewhat selective if not eclectic.

Is the Current Price Decline Likely to Continue?

One of the most frequently cited sources of information on international market prices for food and agricultural commodities is the Food and Agriculture Organization (FAO) of the United Nations. A frequently used FAO graph showing price developments is reproduced in Figure 1. A quick view at the lines in this graph may suggest that prices of major food commodities have declined dramatically in recent months. A naive observer might get the impression that they are in free fall, possibly even approaching zero. It is, though, important

---

[1] For a discussion of the factors that had triggered the price spikes on international food markets as well as an analysis of domestic and international policy responses that could potentially cure the resulting problems for world food security, see Tangermann (2011) and the literature referenced there.

to take a close look at the definition of the vertical axis: it does not start at zero. Graphs constructed that way provide an exaggerated impression of the rates of change of the variables shown in the lines. Moreover, the FAO graph reproduced here covers only a relatively short period.

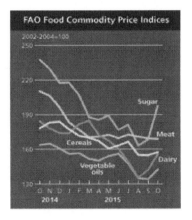

Figure 1: FAO Information on Food Commodity Prices
Source: Reproduced from FAO (2015)

In order to gain a more telling impression of the market situation and its

development we should take a look at the longer term evolution of prices as shown in Figure 2, based on the same type of FAO data. Against the view that prices are on a declining trend—and possibly declining without any floor—longer term perspective shows that even though food prices are currently on the decline, they are still higher than they used to be before the period when the price explosion took place. This is true even if prices are corrected for inflation, as was done for the data shown in Figure 2.

Taking an even longer time period into consideration we must remember that around 40 years ago, i.e., in the mid-1970s, the world also experienced an extraordinary peak of food prices. At that time governments and the international community were equally concerned about world food security and its future, and new policies for agricultural development and new institutions were established, some of which have survived until today. But after that price peak in 1974–1975 prices came down again and continued along their secular decline in real terms.

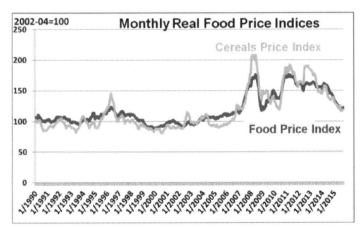

Figure 2: Evolution of Prices for Cereals and Food Since 1990
Source: Based on data available at FAO (2015)

There are, though, reasons to argue that the price spike we have seen more recently in 2007 and subsequent years was of a different nature than what happened in the mid-1970s, even though some of the factors that have triggered the dramatically rising prices in both periods may have been the same. In the 1970s, when the price crisis subsided prices essentially returned to their longer term declining trend in real terms. This time, however, it appears that even though we observe a strong price decline at the moment, international market prices for food and agricultural commodities may not really return to the lower levels that prevailed before 2007. Of course, this is a statement about what might happen in the future and nobody knows with any certainty what will actually happen in the future. Yet, there are institutions that generate price projections, and such projections can provide an impression of where markets may go in the years to come, under all sorts of assumptions regarding the most likely development of the factors determining supply and demand. In well-done projections, these assumptions are explicitly specified and reported in a transparent way.

One institution that has already for quite some time generated projections for world markets for agricultural and food commodities is the OECD (Organisation for Economic Co-operation and Development). Since a number of years the OECD has been joined in this work by the FAO, contributing specific knowledge of the market and policy situation in developing countries. Let us for a moment consider the development of the international price of wheat in real terms as projected by OECD and FAO. The wheat price data presented in Figure 3 first of all remind us of the enormous price peak experienced in the mid-1970s. They also show the depressed though fluctuating price level on international wheat markets prevailing in the years before the 2007–2008 price peak, as well as the much higher price level observed after 2007. The wheat price projected by OECD and

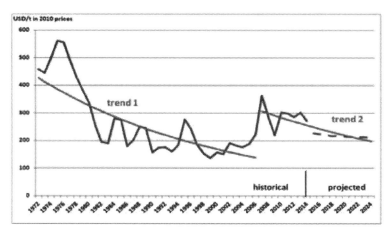

Figure 3: World Market Price for Wheat in Real Terms
Source: Author's calculations based on OECD/FAO (2015)

FAO in their 2015 Outlook, produced at a time when commodity prices had already embarked on their recent much noticed decline, implies a gradual downward movement (in real terms) from their high post-2007 level. Yet, for the 10 year future period covered wheat prices are projected to remain still significantly above their pre-2007 level.[2]

If, contrary to developments in the 1970s, prices for wheat (and other food commodities) should after the more recent peak indeed not return to their pre-2007 level then some sort of a structural change appears to have occurred in the mid-2000s. To provide a graphic impression of the magnitude of that structural shift, the author of this article calculated simple time trends (logarithmic) for the two sub-periods of 1972–2006 and 2007–2024, the latter one including the OECD/FAO projection. As shown in Figure 3, the

trend implicit in the second sub-period is on a significantly higher level than that of the earlier period.

In the international market for rice, some factors driving prices are similar to those working in the wheat market, but there are also differences. In particular, there was an extraordinary price peak on the rice market as well in 2008, but the forces behind that specific price situation for rice had little in common with those behind the price spike on the international market for wheat.[3] Whatever the market situation for rice in recent years may have been, the future evolution of the rice price as projected by OECD/FAO is such that, like in the case of wheat, it is not expected to fall back to the low level prevailing before the 2008 price crisis (see Figure 4). As a matter of fact, the projection even implies a slight increase of the rice price in real terms.

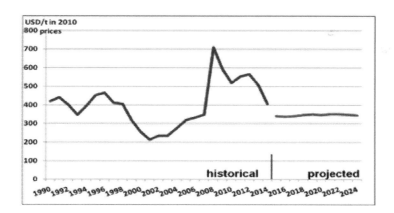

Figure 4: World Market Price for Rice in Real Terms
Source: Author's calculations based on OECD–FAO (2015)

---

[2] The central price projections of OECD/FAO do not include random factors such as weather-caused yield variations. They do, therefore, not exhibit price fluctuations. In reality, prices will of course fluctuate around their longer term trend.

[3] For an analysis of the rice price crisis in 2008 see various chapters in Dawe (2010).

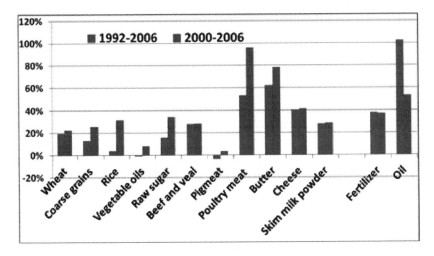

Figure 5: Percentage Change of Real Prices in 2015–2024 (Average) Relative to Two Alternative Base Periods
Source: Author's calculations based on OECD–FAO (2015)

The broader picture across a larger set of agricultural commodities included in the OECD/FAO Outlook indicates that for the average of the 10 year period covered in the market projections, i.e., 2015–2024, nearly all commodities are expected to be at a higher price level in real terms then where they stood on average in the years 1992–2006, i.e., the 15 year period before the price explosion (see the blue bars in Figure 5). And if we take the 7 year period immediately before the price boom of 2007 as the base, relative to that period prices in real terms are expected for most agricultural commodities to be ~20%–30% above the level that we knew before the price boom had occurred (the red bars in Figure 5).

What are the major factors that may explain why we appear to have experienced an upward structural shift in agricultural and food commodity prices, as indicated by such price projections? This is not the place for an extensive treatment of that complex issue. Only three points will be mentioned.[4]

First, agriculture and the food economy are large users of energy and hence closely linked to price developments on energy markets. Rapidly rising oil prices are therefore believed to have been one of the factors behind mounting prices

---

[4] For a much more detailed analysis and discussion, see the annual publications of the OECD/FAO Outlook.

of agricultural commodities in 2007 and subsequent years,[5] and the more recent dramatic decline of oil prices is most likely also one of the reasons why agricultural commodity prices are now declining. Many observers, though, consider the current low level of oil prices to be a transitory phenomenon and expect oil prices to attain a much higher level again in the future. The 2015 OECD/FAO Outlook also expects oil prices to rise again in the future, and this is one of the factors explaining the relatively high expected level of future prices for agricultural and food commodities.

But there are also two more specific agricultural elements in this price picture. One is the fact that, beginning in the early 2000s, a rapidly increasing share of global output of agricultural commodities is being used to produce biofuels, in particular coarse grains and vegetable oils (Figure 6). A share in the order of magnitude of 12%–13% of world output of these two commodities is now taken away from the food market and channeled into a different market, i.e., for energy production. Some of that is happening because of market developments. But the largest part of it—and OECD has analyzed that very carefully—is a result of government policies in the form of mandates, production subsidies, use subsidies, quotas, and other equivalent measures. This means that this totally new factor behind the development of world markets for agricultural commodities is largely policy driven. Within a ~10 year period a very large amount of additional demand that did not exist in the past has entered the market for agricultural products and has certainly driven up prices.[6] It is probably no exaggeration to call this a structural shift of market conditions in world

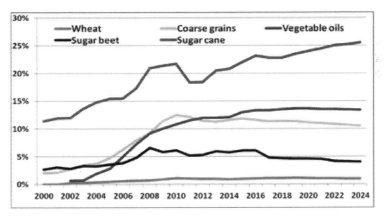

Figure 6: Share of Use for Biofuel Production in Global Output of Selected Agricultural Commodities

Source: Author's calculations based on OECD–FAO (2015)

---

[5] See Tangermann (2011) and the literature referenced there.

[6] For an early analysis of the economic implications of biofuel support policies, including consequences for agricultural commodity markets, see OECD (2008).

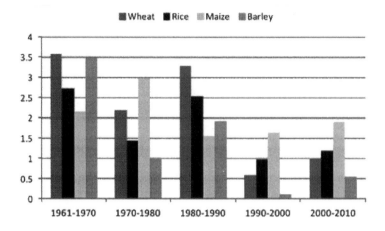

Figure 7: Compound Annual Growth Rates in World Yields per Hectare
Source: Reproduced from Interagency Report to the Mexican G20 Presidency (2012)

agriculture. This part of global demand for agricultural commodities is expected to remain with us largely irrespective of what happens to commodity prices. At the Paris meeting on climate change in the second week of December 2015, many governments have declared that they are determined, for good or not so good reasons, to continue to promote the use of agricultural commodities for the production of biofuels.

Finally, there is another specific agricultural factor behind higher prices on agricultural and food commodity markets, equally worrying as the expansion of biofuel and unfortunately occurring at the same time. It is the fact that yield growth for major cereals and grains has declined in the last two decades or so (see Figure 7). The world has had a green revolution in the past, but it is lacking one in our days. We certainly want to have one again—but

unfortunately it is not occurring for the time being, and there are also no strong signs that it is immediately around the corner. If we combine the decline in yield growth worldwide with additional demand from the biofuel sector and a high growth rate of demand for food from emerging economies—China being one of them— then of course we should not be surprised to find that we have reached a higher price plateau for agricultural commodities.

The interim conclusion is that while prices of agricultural and food commodities are declining at the moment, we should not exaggerate the importance of that decline. There is no doubt that prices are actually declining since a number of months, but they are doing so from the extremely high level they had attained in the years following 2007. There are good reasons to believe that they will not fall below the level of what we have had in the past, with the possible exception of some temporary downward fluctuations. There is a good probability that in the medium term future prices may actually remain above the level experienced before the 2007–2008 price spike. Thus, the assessment of the market situation depends on one's perspective. If it is short term, say the most recent 2 years or so, then prices are certainly declining. If one has a somewhat longer time horizon, comparing the medium-term outlook with what the world was used to before prices suddenly peaked in 2007 and subsequent years, then one has good reasons to identify an increase in the plateau of agricultural and food commodity prices.

Implications for Food Security

Against the background of what was stated earlier about the market outlook, the implications for food security will be discussed here in terms of the consequences of high food prices.

Of course, readers who expect a different market outlook can simply reverse the whole argument by replacing high prices by low or declining prices, and the implications for food security would then be the opposite of what will be suggested here.

Fundamentally the argument is pretty simple. High prices are certainly good for food producers, while they are a problem for food consumers. How a country overall is affected and how individual households fare depends on whether they are net producers or net consumers. The most important question to be asked, therefore, is whether the countries or households concerned produce as much food as they consume and possibly even more, or whether they need to buy food in order to maintain their consumption.

What are the facts regarding that net trade status? First of all, for those countries where food security is potentially or actually a serious problem, i.e., the least

Figure 8: Net Exports of Agricultural Products from Least Developed Countries
Source: FAOSTAT (2015)

developed countries, the situation is rather clear. If we take these countries as a group and look at the most important staple food, namely cereals, then we can see that the least developed countries as a group are a large net importer of cereals, and what is more their net imports of cereals are growing rapidly (see Figure 8).

As a matter of fact, the least developed countries are net importers not only of cereals, but as a group they are also net importers of rice. Moreover, least developed countries as a group are net importers for the whole set of agricultural products taken together, obviously to be expressed not in physical but in monetary terms.

If we look at individual countries, then the picture is obviously more diverse. If the first half of the 1980s is compared with the second half of the 2000s, then we find that a growing share of developing countries in all income groups are net food importers (Figure 9). That trend toward a growing proportion of net food

importers is particularly true for the low-income developing countries. Among the high-income developing countries, 100% of them are net food importers. If we take all developing countries together, 80% of them are now net food importers, and that share is growing.

Obviously, this overall situation does not apply to all individual countries. Thailand is a net exporter of cereals, rice, and even of agricultural products overall (Figure 10). Thus, there are major exceptions among developing countries. But for the group of developing countries overall it remains true that they are net food importers. The implications regarding the interplay between food prices on international markets and food security are obvious. For developing countries as a group, high food prices are a problem rather than a solution. That is not the case, though, for Thailand: a food exporting country of course is happy to see high food prices.

When we move to the level of

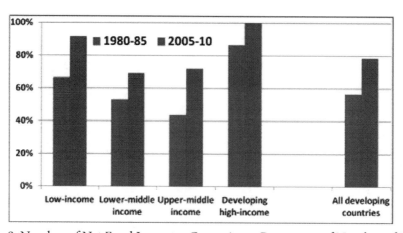

Figure 9: Number of Net Food Importer Countries as Percentage of Number of Developing Countries in Respective Income Group
Source: OECD (2013a; 2013b) based on Matthews (2012).

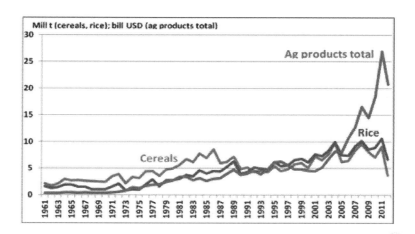

Figure 10: Thailand's Net Exports of Agricultural Products
Source: FAOSTAT (2015)

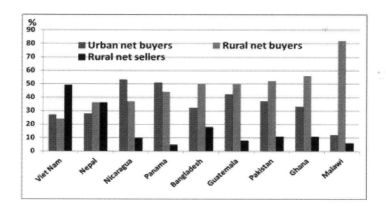

Figure 11: Shares of Net Buyers and Net Sellers of Staple Food in All Households of
Respective Group, Selected Countries
Source: Filipski and Covarrubias (2012).

individual households, the situation in only a few selected individual countries can be presented here (Figure 11, based on findings in Filipski and Covarrubias 2012). What is shown in this figure are the shares of urban respectively rural households that are a net buyers or a net sellers of staple food. We can see that in most developing countries among those shown here there is a good share of urban households that are net buyers.

What may be more surprising, though, is the finding that even among rural households there is a large share of net buyers. Where this is the case, the resources available to these households do not allow them to produce as much food as the family needs. So these households have to go out to the market. The data used in the analysis cited here includes not only grain but also staple food overall, and hence also covers the output generated in

urban gardening and similar activities. Thus, even if many rural households are obviously net sellers of food, among the countries in the particular group shown here their share among all rural households is less than the share of rural net buyers, the only exception among the countries covered here being Vietnam.

What does all that mean? If food prices increase, how does that affect the welfare of individual households? This is shown, for the same set of selected developing countries in Figure 12. Five income quintiles are distinguished in this analysis. To the left, the blue bar represents the impact on the poorest people in the respective country. When food prices rise by 20%, their welfare declines by a rate in the order of magnitude of 4%–6%. Rising food prices also depress welfare among households with higher incomes, though the rate of welfare loss tends

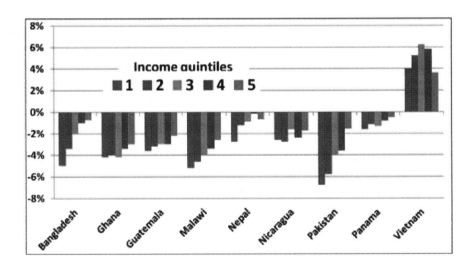

Figure 12: Welfare Impact of a 20% Increase in Price of Staple Food for Alternative Income Quintiles
Source: Filipski and Covarrubias (2012)

to be the smaller the higher the level of income, largely due to Engel's law and the resulting lower share of income spent on food among richer households. Among the countries included here, Vietnam is again the only exception: an increase of food prices is welfare improving for all income quintiles in Vietnam.

The conclusion from all this is that high food prices tend to hurt most developing countries and most individual households in that part of the world.[7]

How Should Policies Respond?

Given that high food prices cause harm to consumers, and the more so the lower the family income is, it is not a good idea for developing country governments to engage in policies, be it domestically or at the border, that support prices of agricultural products at a higher level than the market would generate. While this statement sounds nearly trivial, governments of several developing countries have a tendency to disregard it, placing more weight on the impact of prices on agricultural producers. In many cases this appears to be the case based on the notion that higher prices (and subsidies, be it on inputs or output) provide incentives for farmers to expand output, raising the availability of food on the market. The fact that high prices at the same time make it more difficult for consumers to have access to food appears to be discounted in the process of political decision making. Given that in many developing countries (and in the group of developing countries overall), the volume of food consumption is larger than that of food production, and hence that high prices do more harm than good, there should be more awareness of the negative implication of high-price policies.

However, there are indications that the level of support provided to farmers in developing countries, including support through price raising policies, is on the rise. The measure used in the OECD to quantify the level of support provided by governments is the producer support estimate (PSE). In its percentage version, this indicator expresses the share of total farm revenue that comes from government policies as opposed to markets. As can be seen in Figure 13, in the rich countries, i.e., in the OECD area, this was at the level of around 30%–35% in the mid-1990s and declined to ~20% more recently.

If we set against that a number of selected emerging economies we can see that the level of support they are providing to their agriculture has increased quite a bit in recent years and a good part of that is indeed price support. Among the overall group of countries covered in this analysis, the share of farm

---

[7] This conclusion is obviously derived from a purely static argument. In a dynamic analysis, rising food prices can trigger income growth among food producers and rural workers. Where this results in a shift from net food buyer to net food producer status, rising food prices can have positive welfare implications for the households concerned. However, it will take some time for this effect to dominate. For a more extensive discussion and references to relevant literature, se Filipski and Covarrubias (2012).

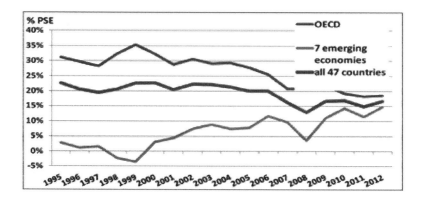

Figure 13: Government Support to Agricultural Producers in the OECD Area and Selected Emerging Economies
Source: OECD (2013a; 2013b)
Note: The seven emerging economies covered in the OECD analysis are Brazil, China, Indonesia, Kazakhstan, Russian Federation, South Africa, and Ukraine.

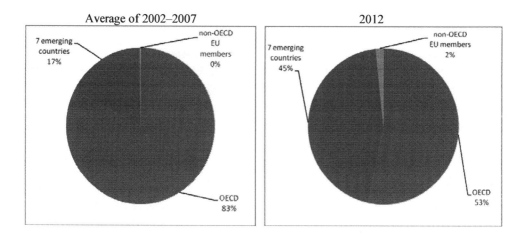

Figure 14: Shares of Country Groups in Aggregate Producer Support of All 47 Countries Covered in the OECD's Analysis of Farm Support
Source: Author's calculations based on PSE database of OECD (2013a; 2013b)

support provided in emerging economies has increased significantly over the last ~10 years (see Figure 14). In other words, governments in the emerging economies covered here, and most likely also in other developing countries, engage in farm policies, including price raising measures that are not really in the interest of food security of their people.

From there we can progress to one eclectic comment on the agricultural negotiations of the World Trade Organization (WTO) Doha Round. One of the issues debated there, very much pushed by a group of developing countries known as the G33, with India being particularly interested in this issue is whether developing countries should be allowed to provide price support to those domestic farmers from which they buy staple food, to be put that into storage for food security reasons. For the time being, WTO rules on domestic farm support under the Agreement on Agriculture impose constraints on the extent to which this is allowed. India has run into problems with that constraint. From an economic point of view, providing farm support in the context of public stockholding for food security purposes is not at all a convincing proposition. Storage policies may be very helpful to be prepared for an emergency situation, but when a government intends to stockpile food it is not at all necessary to provide price support to domestic producers. Food can simply be bought into stockpiles at market prices, and that is exactly what economic reasoning would advise governments to do. Speaking more generally, it should be noted that producer price support is far less efficient than improving the enabling environment for agriculture,

i.e., supporting extension, education, infrastructure, research, technology development, etc. It is not a matter of should one or should one not provide support to agriculture development. It is a matter of the most effective and efficient way of doing so.

More in passing, we should also stress that in the WTO there should be more talk about disciplining export restrictions. A number of countries had embargoed exports in the 2007–2008 period, and that has very much contributed to panic in the market place and among government and, hence, to driving prices up.

Finally, as far as policies are concerned, more needs to be done to support agricultural development and food security in developing countries. Consider the long-term evolution of the share of total Official Development Assistance (ODA) that is channeled into agriculture, shown in Figure 15. We can see that this share had increased considerably after the world food crisis of the mid-1970s. At the time everybody was convinced that the world needed to engage in a serious effort in order to make the world more food secure. But when prices calmed down again, governments simply forgot about their good resolutions, and assistance to agricultural development as a share of overall ODA fell back to the same low level at which it stood before that food crisis erupted.

How does that compare to experience with the more recent world food crisis of 2007–2008 and subsequent years? In Figure 15, we can see a marginal increase of ODA to agriculture after, and possibly in response to, that recent price crisis. Yet, that increase is minimal and it

Figure 15: Share of Assistance to Agriculture, Forestry, and Fisheries in Total Official Development Assistance, 1967–2013
Source: OECD (2015)

appears to be fading away already. That is a very sad story. When prices peaked in 2007–2008 there were great words of promises on the side of policy makers in the G8, the G20, and in other places. But the actual statistics regarding assistance to agriculture in developing countries are far less convincing.

Can one think of an approach that would provide more reliable assistance to agricultural development? In an initiative in the framework of the International Centre for Trade and Sustainable Development and the World Economic Forum we have come up with one suggestion which is somewhat original. It is a new instrument that could be agreed at the international level,

establishing some sort of a link between what governments in the better-off countries do for their farmers and what the international community does for agricultural development in the poorer countries.[8] The approach proposed is that as a first step one measures the level of support provided to farmers in the industrialized and emerging countries, i.e., in the richer part of the world. Any measure of support to agriculture in these richer countries could be used, e.g., the one that is being discussed in the Doha Round negotiations of the WTO, i.e., the Overall Trade Distorting Support (OTDS). And as a second step of the proposal the countries in the richer part of the world would provide their assistance

---

[8] For more detail on this proposal and for a more general discussion of where international policies for agriculture should go in the years to come, see Tangermann (2016).

to agricultural development in the poorer countries meeting agreed quantifiable criteria, in an agreed proportion to what these richer countries do for their domestic farmers. Just to suggest an idea of relevant orders of magnitude, if one were to take no >1% of what governments do for farmers in rich countries and channel that amount into agricultural development in the poorer countries, that would increase current ODA to agriculture by ~20%. Thus, a small proportion of government support to farmers in the richer countries could do a lot to improve the prospects for agricultural development in the poorer countries. And as this approach would not raise food prices in the recipient developing countries, it would also not do any harm to poor consumers. This concrete element of financial solidarity between richer and poorer countries could do a lot to improve food security and agricultural development in countries.

Conclusions

There are good reasons to believe that the "new normal" on markets for agricultural and food products may be a higher level of food prices than the world was used to before the price peak in 2007–2008 and subsequent years. Of course this is not a certain outcome, but one that appears to have a significant probability. However, nobody knows with any certainty what is going to happen to markets in the years to come. Given that uncertainty the international trade regime should be prepared for both high and low food prices.

In the past, the WTO and its predecessor, the GATT, focused on depressed prices and tried to discipline policies that contributed to price depression. In other words, the international trade regime was traditionally focused on limiting farm support so as to act against depressed food prices. There is no reason to discard that orientation altogether. However, to be on the safe side the WTO should also do more to guard against high food prices. One of the options available and worthy of a negotiating effort is a more effective and operational discipline on export restrictions.

The international community should certainly also do more to improve food security in developing countries. One option in that regard is to establish a link between the benefits governments in rich countries provide to their domestic farmers on the one hand, and what they do on the other hand for agricultural development and food security in the poorer countries.

As far as domestic policies in developing countries are concerned, there is reason to reconsider the price support policies pursued by many governments through both border measures and domestic instruments. Quite apart from efficiency considerations, which also speak against such price support policies, in most developing countries these policies do more harm to food consumers than they provide benefits to farmers. And where price support comes in the guise of improving food security, e.g., through public stockholding for food security purposes, one should be particularly skeptical. There are much more effective and efficient ways of improving food security and at the same time fostering agricultural development.

References

Dawe, D., ed. 2010. *The Rice Crisis—Markets, Policies and Food Security.* London, Washington, DC: FAO and Earthscan.

FAO. 2015. "FAO Food Price Index." http://www.fao.org/worldfoodsituation/foodpricesindex/en/ (visited on November 24, 2015).

FAOSTAT. 2015. "Data download facility." http://faostat3.fao.org/download/T/TP/E (visited on November 2, 2015).

Filipski, M., and K. Covarrubias. 2012. "Distributional Impacts of Commodity Prices in Developing Countries." In *Agricultural Policies for Poverty Reduction,* ed. J. Brooks. Paris: OECD.

Interagency Report to the Mexican G20 Presidency. 2012. *Sustainable Agricultural Productivity Growth and Bridging the Gap for Small Family Farms.* Paris: OECD.

Matthews, A. 2012. *Agricultural Trade and Food Security.* Background paper prepared for OECD. Dublin: Trinity College.

OECD. 2008. *Biofuel Support Policies—An Economic Assessment.* Paris: OECD.

OECD. 2013a. *Agricultural Policy Monitoring and Evaluation 2013: OECD Countries and Emerging Economies.* Paris: OECD.

OECD. 2013b. *Global Food Security: Challenges for the Food and Agricultural System.* Paris: OECD.

OECD. 2015. "Query Wizard for International Development Statistics." http://stats.oecd.org/qwids/... (visited on November 24, 2015).

OECD/FAO. 2015. OECD-FAO *Agricultural Outlook 2015-2024.* Paris: OECD.

Tangermann, S. 2011. *Policy Solutions to Agricultural Market Volatility: A Synthesis.* ICTSD Programme on Agricultural Trade and Sustainable Development, Issue Paper No. 33. Geneva: International Centre for Trade and Sustainable Development. http://ictsd.org/i/publications/108969/.

Tangermann, S. 2016. *Agriculture and Food Security: New Challenges and Options for International Policy.* E15 Expert Group on Agriculture, Trade and Food Security—Policy Options Paper. E15Initiative. Geneva: International Centre for Trade and Sustainable Development (ICTSD) and World Economic Forum.

World Food Policy - Volume 2 Issue 2/Volume 3 Issue 1, Fall 2015/Spring 2016

Food Security In an Age of Falling Commodity and Food Prices: The Case of Sub-Saharan Africa

Gérard Azoulay[A]

Within a context characterized by a simultaneous occurrence of a global equilibrium of the world food balance and the persistence of a high percentage of the world's population that does not adequately meet its nutritional needs, this article intends to concentrate on the impacts of falling food prices on food security focusing on Sub-Saharan Africa (SSA). SSA is not the region that accounts for the most important number of people suffering from hunger, but is a region that experiences the highest prevalence of hunger.

The article considers the driving forces of the rising/falling prices of food and commodities. It analyzes the impact of falling food prices on the food security situation in SSA, and discusses the main constraints of food policies and strategies in SSA.

Keywords: Food, prices, food security, policies, Sub-Saharan Africa

Introduction

The strong growth of world food production during the past 50 years did not bring to an end the diverse manifestations of hunger. We can observe a simultaneous occurrence of a global equilibrium of the world food balance and the persistence of a high percentage of the world's population that does not adequately meet its nutritional needs: 795 million people fail to adequately satisfy their nutritional needs, 1.3 billion people live on <1 dollar a day, and suffer from nutritional deficiencies in micronutrients and macronutrients.

These 795 million people are unable to produce or to buy what is needed to live. Those who are hungry are not predominantly consumers who do not have enough money to buy their food. They are mainly producers of agricultural products: 75% live in rural areas and among them, 90% are poor peasants and farm workers; the remaining 25% are sentenced to the exodus by poverty, poor peasants who live in the city, in shanty towns or camps. This rural migration represents ~50 to 60 million people per year. Hunger is not only a consequence of poverty, but also one of its causes, undermining the productive potential of individuals (Azoulay, 2006).

[A] Université Paris Sud.

doi: 10.18278/wfp.2.2.3.1.10

Within this overall context, this article attempts to concentrate on the impacts of falling prices of food and commodities on food security focusing on Sub-Saharan Africa (SSA). SSA is not the region that accounts for the most important number of people suffering from hunger, but the region which knows the highest prevalence of hunger.

The article is divided into three parts: in the first part, the driving forces of the rising/falling prices of food and commodities are considered. In the second part, the impacts of falling food prices on the food security situation in SSA are examined. Finally, the main constraints of food policies and strategies in SSA are discussed.[1]

The Driving Forces of the Rising/Falling Prices of Food and Commodities

The Food Price Trend

During several decades world food prices used to be depressed by the dumping of surpluses by western nations. But after 2005, and specifically in 2008, food prices globally rose to unprecedented levels. Prices increased again in mid-2011, exceeding 2008 levels and remaining relatively high through 2011.

There was a strong belief that the world had entered a new era of not just high but also rising and volatile food prices, in contrast to previous decades characterized by low prices.

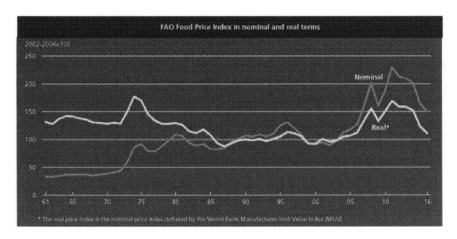

Figure 1: Food Price Index in Nominal and Real Terms: 1961–2016
Source: FAO Food Price Index: http://www.fao.org/worldfoodsituation/foodpricesindex/en/

---

[1] This article was presented and discussed in a round table at the International Conference on World Food Policy: Future Faces of Food and Farming; Regional Challenges; Bangkok 17–18 December 2015, organized by The Royal Society of Thailand.

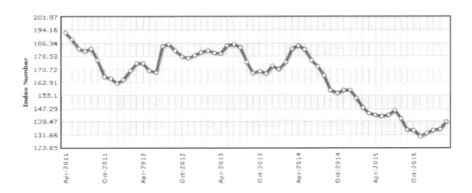

Figure 2: Commodity Food Price Index Monthly Price—Index Number
Apr 2011–Mar 2016: −53.070 (−27.59%)
Source: http://www.indexmundi.com/commodities/?commodity=food-price-index&months=60

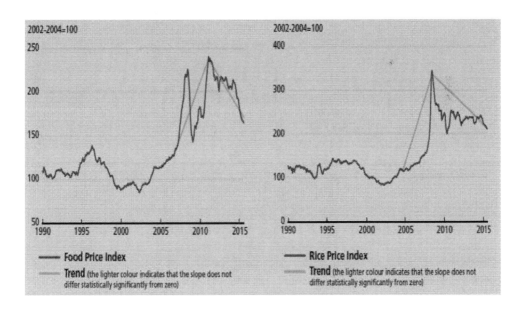

Figure 3: Food Price Trend and Rice Trend

But, prices of food commodities have started to decline since the beginning of 2011 and they have suddenly fallen steeply since May 2014. The nominal FAO Food Price Index (FPI) (FAO b, 2016) has fallen, almost uninterruptedly, between March 2014 and the beginning of 2016. For instance, the FPI lost ~50 points (a quarter of its value) between 2014 and 2015 and recently slumped to a 6 year low of 149,3 points in January 2016.

A statistically significant upward shift in trend is as remarkable from August 2006 to January 2011 as a downward shift from January 2011 to the present. As the following graph indicates, the FPI as well as the rice price index decreased sharply since 2011 (rice being a major cereal in the diet of a large part of SSA population, especially in urban areas which include >50% of population).

As the FAO indicates, since 2008, the cereal indices have exhibited progressively lower volatility after each successive change point and price behavior has reverted to that before the 2008 episode, in which prices were widely regarded as falling and with lower volatility. Rice is the only commodity showing a comparable change in trend. In terms of variability, both grains and rice exhibit behavior similar to the FPI, but with an additional change point during the period of elevated volatility.

The fall in the FPI is the result of sharp declines in the prices of rice, grains, sugar, and vegetable oils, but not all foodstuffs have followed these trends. According to the FAO, agricultural commodities are going through a period of lower and less volatile prices.

The Driving Forces of the Decline of Food and Commodity Prices

This decline of food prices is similar to the decline of the prices of commodities. The index underwent statistically significant changes both in trend and volatility: a period of higher volatility between 2006 and 2011 coincides with an upward trend, followed by a downward trend and lower volatility starting in 2011.

In the most recent period (April 2011 to October 2015), the commodity price index decreased from 208 to 100 with a sharp decline from summer 2014. Going back to the driving forces that explained the 2008 sudden escalation of food prices, it seems useful to examine which of these driving forces have lost all pertinence and reversed drastically during the last two years and subsequently, explore the opposite forces that could explain the down trend in the last period. Then it could be of interest to assess the prospective impact of some remaining forces still pertinent today, if any.

Conjectural and structural driving forces could explain the 2008 price surge (Azoulay 2012). Several conjectural forces occurs: a reduced production due to climatic change (floods in Australia and Argentina, dry weather drought and fires in Russia, and jellies threatening crops in Europe and North America); the levels of historically low stocks (19.4% in 2007/2008); the higher cost of energy and transport (the Reuters-CRB energy index having tripled since 2003); an increased production of bio fuels (100 million tons of cereals, 4.7% of the global production of cereals were used in 2007–2008, a large diversion of agricultural land to

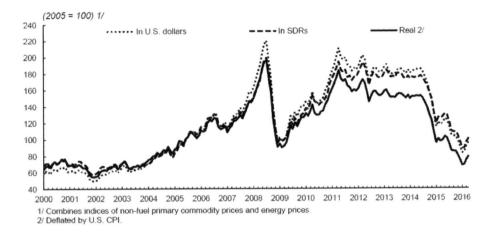

(2005 = 100) 1/

1/ Combines indices of non-fuel primary commodity prices and energy prices.
2/ Deflated by U.S. CPI.

Figure 4 : Commodity Price Index—2000–2016
Source: International Monetary Fund—IMF Primary Commodity Prices

produce biofuels: ethanol from maize and synthetic diesel from vegetable oils); some trade policies (export reduction in some countries aiming to reduce the impact of prices on vulnerable groups); the speculative money involved in commodities markets (the amount of speculative funds invested in agricultural commodity futures markets increased from $5 billion in 2000 to 175 billion in 2007).

Beside these conjectural driving forces, some underlying structural ones played a major long-term role: the changing consumption patterns in some major emerging countries (during more than a decade, China, Brazil, and India—40% of the world population— experienced a strong growth which implies the development of a middle class which tends to adopt a different diet including more meat and dairy products); the decline of investment in agriculture (agricultural investment was

largely ruined in SSA countries under structural adjustment. Investment has been affected by the reduction of public spending and subsidies to the agricultural sector); and the "urban bias" and the so-called "archaism" of the agricultural sector (Lipton 1977). Agriculture has been traditionally regarded as an archaic sector, often mistreated by Governments of developing countries. That was the case for the economic policies implemented in SSA, implying low urban consumer price and taxation of domestic agricultural production prices detrimental to small producers.

Have these conjectural and structural driving forces reversed drastically, that could then explain this recent decline? Since 2008, some of these forces reversed and contributed to explain the decline, but some forces still remain operative. The main cause of the decline was primarily the fact that supplies were higher than expected. In

2014–2015, the world cereal supply was estimated to be 20% more than demand. The world stock-to-use ratio was 25.2% in 2014–2015. Abundant supplies keep international prices under pressure. Supplies and stocks of the major grains are still very strong (25.2% versus 19.4% in 2007/2008), even if estimates for 2015–2016 indicate a tiny decrease of world cereal production (FAO 2016). The cost of energy has reached minimal value (see below figure 5). Trade policies based on export reduction are no more applied in some countries.

But some driving forces of the 2008 situation did not reverse at all: the increased production of bio fuels; (the speculative money involved in commodities markets; and the structural changing consumption patterns in some major emerging countries; all these factors are still contributing to push the food prices up.

The Correlation between Food and Oil Prices

In the past 18 months, fossil fuel prices have seen a decline by more than half. During the last 25 years, agricultural commodity prices were interconnected with energy prices. This interconnection derives from both demand and supply sides. Mainly the growing mechanization of agriculture has increased the influence of energy prices on production costs, and hence, output prices. Falling oil prices are likely to have subdued the competitive demand for biofuels and, consequently, the derived demand for agricultural feedstocks, which, in turn, reduced their own prices (maize and sugar, and to some extent wheat, used as feedstocks for biofuel production).

The correlation between the two series, especially since 2007, is very pronounced mainly because of increased influence of energy prices on production

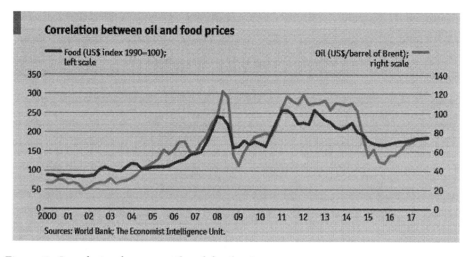

Figure 5: Correlation between oil and food prices

costs, and hence, on output prices by the growing mechanization of world agriculture.

Oil was $25 a barrel in 2003 but soared to almost $148 in 2008. In July 2014, the price of Brent crude has been ~$110 a barrel. But this has now fallen to $40 a barrel at January 2016.

What about Macroeconomic Factors?

Macroeconomic factors play an important role in impacting the falling / rising trend of food commodities prices.

According to the FAO, extreme price volatility has been extremely rare in agricultural markets, but the global food system is becoming increasingly vulnerable to it and susceptible to episodes of extreme volatility, as markets are increasingly integrated in the world economy. Extreme price volatility in global agricultural markets means rising and more frequent threats to world food security.

Volatility connotes two principal concepts: variability and uncertainty; the former describing overall movement and the latter referring to movement that is unpredictable. However, the efficiency of the price system begins to break down when price movements are increasingly uncertain and subject to extreme swings over an extended period of time.

Furthermore, despite of a rise in liquidity, inflation is very low and even negative in a few developed countries. Real commodity prices are falling. The most common explanation is the global economic slowdown, which has diminished demand for energy, minerals, and agricultural products.

The appreciation of the United States dollar (USD) against major currencies (reaching a 13 year high in September 2015) is significant because international commodity prices have typically had an inverse relationship with the value of the USD. When the USD strengthens against other major currencies (euro and yen), commodity prices typically fall. On the other hand, when the value of the USD weakens against other major currencies, the prices of commodities increase. This relationship is largely a result of commodities being priced in USD and of international buyers being required to purchase them with USD. When the value of the dollar rises, buyers have less purchasing power and so demand typically weakens and symmetrically.

The correlation between commodity prices and interest rates is an additional macroeconomic factor. There is a negative correlation between falling real interest rates and commodity prices. In the 1970s, in 2002–2004, and 2007–2008 falling real interest rates were accompanied by rising real commodity prices. In a situation of large liquidity, the money flows also into commodities, and so bids their prices up and thus that prices fall when interest rates rise (Frankel 2014). According to Frankel, high interest rates strengthen the domestic currency, thereby reducing the price of internationally traded commodities in domestic terms (even if the price has not fallen in foreign currency terms).

Increased vulnerability is being triggered by an apparent increase in extreme weather events; a greater reliance on international trade to meet food needs at the expense of stock holding; a growing demand for food commodities from other sectors, especially energy; and a faster transmission of macroeconomic factors onto commodity markets, including exchange rate volatility and monetary policy shifts, such as changing interest rate regimes.

Furthermore, financial firms are progressively investing in commodity derivatives as a portfolio hedge because returns in the commodity sector seem uncorrelated with returns to other assets. Evidence suggests that trading in futures markets may have amplified volatility in the short term.

Falling Food Prices and Food Security in SSA

The Food Security Situation

In SSA, fewer than one in four (or 23.2% of the population) are likely to be undernourished in 2014–2016.

This is the highest prevalence and the second in absolute terms, as the region has ~220 million people suffering from hunger in 2014–2016. In fact, the number of undernourished people has increased by 44 million between 1990–1992 and 2014–2016, despite the decline in the prevalence of undernourishment, which reveals the strength of the growth rate of the population (2.7% per year).

Undernourishment around the world, 1990–92 to 2014–16

	Number of undernourished (millions) and prevalence (%) of undernourishment									
	1990–92		2000–02		2005–07		2010–12		2014–16*	
	No.	%	No.	%	No.	%	No.	%	No.	%
WORLD	1 010.6	18.6	929.6	14.9	942.3	14.3	820.7	11.8	794.6	10.9
DEVELOPED REGIONS	20.0	<5.0	21.2	<5.0	15.4	<5.0	15.7	<5.0	14.7	<5.0
DEVELOPING REGIONS	990.7	23.3	908.4	18.2	926.9	17.3	805.0	14.1	779.9	12.9
Africa	181.7	27.6	210.2	25.4	213.0	22.7	218.5	20.7	232.5	20.0
Northern Africa	6.0	<5.0	6.6	<5.0	7.0	<5.0	5.1	<5.0	4.3	<5.0
Sub-Saharan Africa	175.7	33.2	203.6	30.0	206.0	26.5	205.7	24.1	220.0	23.2

Figure 6: Undernourishment around the world,
Source: FAO; State of Food Insecurity 2015

Ranking/score table of all regions		
Overall Rank	*Region*	*2014 GFSI Score*
1	North America	80.0
2	Europe	75.4
3	Middle East and North Africa	57.4
4	Central and South America	56.0
5	Asia and Pacific	55.0
6	Sub-Saharan Africa	36.1

Figure 7: The food Security Situation in SSA
Source: Global Food Security Index 2014

SSA received the lowest regional score in the 2015 Global Food Security Index 2014 (GFSI), with an overall score almost 20 points below that of Asia & Pacific. It also scores the lowest in each of the components of the food security concept (access=affordability, availability, and quality and safety categories).

Hunger, Poverty, and Growth

According to FAO, 18 SSA countries have met the target 1c of the Millennium Development Goals of 2000, with the objective of reducing the prevalence of hunger by 50%, and 4 others are close to reach it.

Among these 18 countries, 7 have also achieved the more ambitious objective of the World Food Summit of 1996 with the objective of reducing by a half the number of people suffering from hunger (Angola, Cameroon, Djibouti, Gabon, Ghana, Mali and Sao Tome, and Principe) and 2 others (South Africa and Togo) are close to doing so.

Although SSA has experienced high economic growth rates over the past 5 years, poverty has not been reduced drastically. SSA has accounted for 8 of the world's 20 fastest-growing economies over the past 5 years (2009–2013). According to the World Bank, economic growth in SSA will reach in 2015, 3.7% instead of 4.6% shown in 2014, which is the lowest growth since 2009. Still, 42.7% of the population live under the poverty headcount ratio at $1.90 a day in 2012 (56.8% in 1990) that means an estimated 50% of the population continues to live on <US$1.25 (weighted at PPP rates) per day.

However, improvements in the structures that impact food security, rather than income improvements, are driving positive changes in SSA. The high economic growth rates that SSA has experienced in recent years have resulted in increased investment in the structures that are necessary to ensure food security. Major improvements have occurred in the presence of food safety-net programs, the existence of crop storage facilities, the percentage of food loss, and the existence of nutritional standards.

Despite high economic growth rate, the numbers of poor people did not decrease in SSA, even if some components of the Human Development Index (UNDP 2015) and the index itself have known a modest improvement (0.518 in 2014 versus 0.499 in 2010).

In this context, the impact of fallen food prices on food security is equivocal.

The Uncertain Impacts of Fallen Food Prices on Food Security

In low-income SSA countries, the urban poor are net food consumers, while small farmers are, generally, net sellers. Rising prices hurt consumers by reducing their purchasing power but benefit producers by increasing their profits. Rising food prices for basic staple food is not beneficial for Africa's poor who consume more food than what they can produce, particularly poor families living in cities that spend the majority of their income on basic foodstuffs. Rising food prices are also having important macroeconomic impacts on many African countries since more food is being imported from the world market leading to worsening balances of trade (only 5% of Africa's imports of cereals come from other African countries).

Lower food prices relative to incomes benefit to food security, by making food acquisition more affordable especially to poor consumers. Food purchases typically account for a significant share of overall household income of the poor in SSA. Overall benefits would, however, be depending on whether households are net buyers of food. At the same time, lower prices also diminish producers' returns. At the country level, low international food prices would also benefit those countries that rely to a large extent on imported food products, as long as their currencies do not decrease as to annihilate the gains from low prices.

Consumers may benefit from the low prices of imported food in particular when these prices result from developed countries farm subsidies. But this situation is largely hazardous as the recent price surge demonstrates, while at the same time small farmers face enormous difficulties in trying to expand production in response to higher prices.

Falling prices may impact on farmers' profitability, reducing investments, and increasing unsustainable agricultural practices. Low returns could reduce incentives for larger investment in agriculture (rural infrastructure, credit availability, input services, research, and extension). As it was explained earlier, underinvestment in agriculture has been considered as one of the main structural causes for the sharp price increases of 2007–2008.

Finally, lower food prices have intensively contributed to reduce (or even partially destroy) domestic agricultural activities. SSA experimented shrinkage of some agricultural sectors due to imports surges generated by low subsidized imports prices: the case of European products (for instance European poultry). Founded on a list of "'infant industry" argument, a domestic development process in agriculture in SSA is extremely difficult to implement under the competition of largely subsidized imported products.

Constraints on Food Policies and Strategies in SSA: Some Prospects

Population Prospects

The world population is projected to increase by >1 billion people within the next 15 years, reaching 8.5 billion in 2030, and to increase further to 9.7 billion in 2050 and 11.2 billion by 2100. Ten years ago, world population was growing by 1.24% per year. Today, the growth rate is 1.18% per year that leads to an additional 83 million people annually.

During 2015–2050, half of the population growth is expected to be concentrated in 9 countries: India, Nigeria, Pakistan, Democratic Republic of the

Major area	Population (millions)			
	2015	*2030*	*2050*	*2100*
World	7 349	8 501	9 725	11 213
Africa	1 186	1 679	2 478	4 387
Asia	4 393	4 923	5 267	4 889
Europe	738	734	707	646
Latin America and the Caribbean	634	721	784	721
Northern America	358	396	433	500
Oceania	39	47	57	71

Figure 8: Population of the World and Major Areas according to the Medium-Variant Projection
Source: United Nations, Department of Economic and Social Affairs. Population Division (2015). World Population Prospects: The 2015 Revision. New York: United Nations.

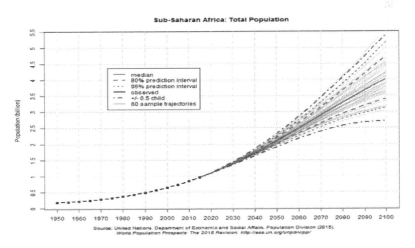

Figure 9: Sub-Saharan Africa: total population

Congo, Ethiopia, Republic of Tanzania, United States of America, Indonesia, and Uganda.

The median-variant projection put the ASS population to 2 billion in 2050 and 4 billion in 2100. From 2000 to 2030, SSA population shall more than double (i.e., the most rapid growth rate of population in the world).

In SSA, fertility rates are among the highest in the world. Women currently average 5.2 children, escalating to 7.6 in Niger, compared to averages of 1.6 in Europe, and 1.9 in North America. In West Africa, a region where malnutrition remains a challenge, fertility rates have declined modestly in the past 60 years, from 6.3 to 5.7 children per mother and in central Africa, a region including some of the poorest African nations, fertility rates have increased from 5.99 to 6.17 since 1950. The pressure on governments to deliver basic services as education, health care, and, most importantly jobs is increasing.

This huge population growth could be seen as an opportunity, as African countries also had the world's fastest economic growth rates. But more convincingly, an alternative approach considers that in this region where food security will remain an extremely severe challenge, an equivalent level of growth of agricultural productivity must be reached to sustain this population growth. Such a level of agricultural productivity growth

to meet the food demand gap is likely unreachable.

The Food Demand Gap

According to the 2014 Global Agricultural Productivity Report, 15% of total SSA demand can be met by maintaining the current total factor productivity (TFP)[2] growth rate.

Demand for food will continue to increase, it is projected to double by 2020, and consumers will be increasingly located in Africa's rapidly growing cities. In SSA, the average annual growth in food demand is projected to be 2.83% per year from 2000 to 2030, primarily due to population increase. Urbanization is accelerating (the share of the world's people living in urban areas will increase from 54% to 66% by 2050). More people in cities will be increasingly diverse their diets. Diet diversification and access to high-quality protein are increasing rapidly in less developing countries. For example, SSA experienced the largest score increase in dietary intake of quality protein (+7.1).[3]

By 2050, the world's middle class is expected to grow from 50% to 70% of the population, with most change taking place in developing countries. According to the African Development Bank,[4] Africa attend the emergence of a middle class, actually estimated, one third of the African population (313 million—34.3%)

---

[2] TFP is the ratio of agricultural outputs (gross crop and livestock output) to inputs (land, labor, fertilizer, machinery, and livestock).

[3] Global FS Index 2015.

[4] BAD, April 2011.

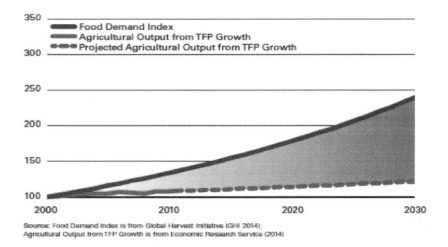

Figure 10: Food Demand Compared to Agricultural Output in SSA, 2000–2030

against 111 million (26.2% of the population) in 1980. The middle class is composed by those who spend between $2 and $20 per day (which is a very large and imprecise definition).

Increased demand for livestock, poultry, and fish is the largest driver in the world food economy and is expected to double by 2050, with 70% of the increase coming from developing countries. As grains and oilseeds are a major part of animal diets and, accordingly, demand for them will also grow substantially.

Income growth is leading to dietary changes and rapid increases in the amounts of processed and perishable foods consumed. Households' own production will likely account for decreasing shares of household consumption.

The current food demand gap is significant, and will become much greater taking in account the SSA population growth rate, the increase of the number of poor despite the increase of an emerging middle class, unless SSA accelerates productivity growth rates and succeeds in alleviate its structural constraints.

Considerable Resources and Agricultural Structural Constraints in SSA

SSA experiences an abundance of agricultural resources (land and water) and has a huge potential to produce food staples, but these resources are largely unexploited because of structural constraints. Farming is largely done under rainfed conditions. Levels of irrigation are very low and make it vulnerable to the changing climate. Natural water supplies are abundant but evenly distributed. SSA has not been able to intensify its agricultural production through irrigation and improved water management. Less than a quarter of the total land area of SSA suitable for rainfed crop production is so used. FAO has estimated that the potential additional land area available for cultivation amounts to more than 700 million ha[5].

SSA also experiences a large variety of agro-ecological environments, farming systems, and large number of staples. This substantial potential to produce food staples remains unexploited because of the same structural constraints.

Despite this rich agricultural potential, the continent increasingly imports from outside of the region to satisfy demand (almost $68 billion in 2014 on $1486 billion world exports). Many of SSA least developed countries have become increasingly dependent on imported food in recent decades. This dependency may not be a serious issue, as long as other export sectors can be developed to generate revenue to pay for food imports. But in many cases, this has not been achieved.

According to FAO, in SSA, the imports bill of food products in some countries is very high related to the gross domestic product (GDP). During periods of rising commodity prices, these countries spent on average up to 5% or 6% of their GDP to import food. For Sierra Leone, the proportion was even 22% to 24% of its GDP to commercial food imports. During the 2000s, agricultural exports from Africa increased fourfold, but imports rose 2.5 times faster, widening the agricultural trade deficit.

SSA is facing structural constraints. Smallholder agriculture is the predominant form of farm organization. Small farming systems is the most important employment and income source for more than two thirds of SSA active workers, especially women, the young, and the poor. More than 70% of the poor reside in rural areas, and most depend on agriculture for food production. In SSA, 13 major farming systems were identified with the 5 largest systems, including maize mixed or highland perennial systems, supporting 65% of Africa's rural population (Garrity, Dixon, & Boffa 2012).

Most farming in SSA is highly fragmented and has a very low labor productivity due to little use of mechanization, fertilizer, pesticides, irrigation, and also due to very limited public support (for instance, measured by ESP), which undermines agricultural output and makes the region a net food importer.

Less than 4% of cropland is irrigated, compared with 35% to 40% in much of Asia. Farmers apply <8 kg per hectare of inorganic fertilizer nutrients (nitrogen, phosphorus, and potash) compared with >150 kg per hectare in much of Asia. As a result, yields of both cereals and tuber crops are low in comparison to the rest of the world (Tittonell and Giller 2013). For instance, a yield gap analysis of cassava in the East African Highlands found a gap of 12.2 t ha, 59% of which was attributed to fertilizers, 28% to genetic differences, and 12% to planting method (Fermont et al. 2009).

Increased production resulted rather from agricultural area expansion often at the expense of the natural resource base. Agricultural productivity in SSA has suffered from decades of policy neglect, years of underinvestment, and extractive practices. Agricultural infrastructure is very weak as the public commitment to

---

[5] Only 10% of the Guinea Savannah, covering an estimated 600 million hectares, is farmed.

agricultural research and development was inefficient. Weak market institutions, ineffective crop storage facilities, high percentage of food loss, fragile logistics services and distribution channels, fragile input and output market access, lack of adequate credit system to small farmers, lack of training, and use of news cultural methods and technologies are frequent failures of agricultural policies. Agricultural and food security policies are extremely weak and not consistent in the long term. The situation results from inefficient and fragile institutions, weakened government, and public institutions effectiveness, sometimes political instability, corruption, or conflicts.

Potential for Greater Productivity: A Critical Issue

Intensification of agricultural production is essential in the more densely populated areas in order to feed the rapidly growing and urbanizing population in SSA.

To remediate the current situation, an "African Green Revolution" is sometimes proposed (Otsuka and Larson 2012). But sustainable intensification of small farming systems is probably the most accurate element of agricultural policy in SSA. This process is generally based on three basic elements: (1) production of more food, feed, fuel, and/or fiber per unit of land, labor, and/or capital used; (2) preservation of ecosystem services, including those governed by healthy soils; and (3) resilience to shocks and stresses, including climate change (Pretty 2014). Sustainable intensification of small farming systems recognizes

that enhanced productivity needs to be consistent with the maintenance of other ecosystem services and enhanced resilience to shocks.

Increasing productivity in a sustainable way for small farming systems in SSA will require new technologies that are appropriate and adaptable for African smallholder farmers and pastoralists and suitable for local agro-environmental conditions at different scales (region, village, and farm). The heterogeneity of smallholder farming systems suggests that processes for sustainable intensification will need to be flexible and adapted to local agro-ecological and socioeconomic conditions. Wealthier farmers can move into the process with investments into knowledge acquisition (Pretty 2011). For poorer households, more incentive structures would be required, provided that such household can move out of the poverty trap.

In any case, enhanced productivity requires access to agro-inputs, profitable output markets, and access to credit, rural infrastructure, marketing, processing and storage organization, reduction of post-harvest losses, and proper access to agricultural knowledge, services, and information. Government investments and policy frameworks will be crucial, including facilitating private sector engagement. In this case, policy regulations, incentives, and coherent intervention strategies across national, regional, community, and farm scales appear essential.

Doubling agricultural output to meet demand and alleviate hunger will increase pressure on already-stressed resources, requiring greater efficiency in agriculture and food systems. Sustainable expansion of land for agriculture will require careful selection, land use management practices, and conservation approaches to prevent desertification and rainforest destruction.

The recent re-engagement of governments in the agricultural sector is improving the socio-organizational conditions in many African countries (Benin 2011). Government investments in agriculture and infrastructure begun in the wake of the food price shocks of 2007–2008 and have also been crucial to improving food security.

The Comprehensive Africa Agriculture Development Program (CAADP), a continent wide framework for accelerating agricultural development was initiated 10 years ago with a major objective: 10% of public expenditures dedicated to agriculture (Conference of Ministers of Agriculture of the African Union. 2003). Following this policy, public agricultural expenditures increased by 7.7% for Africa as a whole in 2003–2008 but decreased by −1.34% in 2008–2013 in the aftermath of the 2007–2008 food and financial crises (due to the fall of governments' fiscal revenues and overall expenditures). Africa's share of public agricultural expenditures in total public expenditures globally decreased from 3.7% in 2003–2008 to 3.1% in 2008–2013, falling short of the CAADP 10% target.

A long-term comprehensive agricultural and food security strategy is still crucial including: production policies (infrastructures, irrigation, inputs, credit, production structures, etc.), internal trade (storage facilities, transportation, credit, market structure, market information system, etc.), and consumption policies (income, health and nutrition, early warning system, etc.) and more basically, sound trade and price policies.

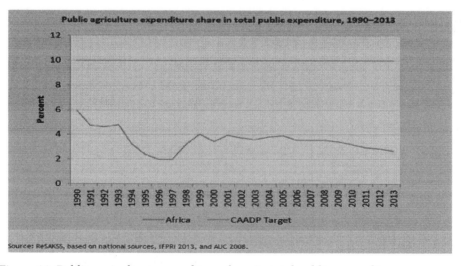

Figure 11: Public agriculture expenditure share in total public expenditure

Regional Integration Attempts and Their Limits

Regional integration has been a longstanding objective of the African Union (for instance the 1980 Lagos plan). Multiple integration organizations exist, but SSA experienced low levels of intra-regional trade resulting from physical and institutional barriers which are a limit to agricultural production and food security.

FAO estimates that African cereal imports in 2008 were US$15.2 billion, just 5% of all grain imported from regional sources (probably a little more underestimates taking in account intra-regional informal trade). The volume of extra-regional food staple imports shows how regional integration in the food staple market can achieve food security.

According to Rakotoarisoa, Lafrate and Paschali 2011, "the increase in food imports since the mid-1970s has been particularly striking for basic foodstuffs such as dairy products, edible oils and fats, meat and meat products, sugar and especially cereals, implying that food import has been increasingly important in ensuring food security."

The idea of a "protected regional market" has been discussed a long time ago (Acts of the Mindelo Conference, 1-6 December 1986) in the context of the Permanent Interstate Committee for Drought Control in the Sahel. Increased regional trade has the potential to expand the size of Africa's market for food staples, boost agricultural growth in surplus zones, and mitigate shortages in deficit ones. In addition, regional trade in food staples can also help moderate price volatility in African food staple markets.

A Common External Tariff (CET) is a basic feature of the Customs Union as a form of economic integration. This trade policy instrument is usually implemented when a less advanced grouping is aimed at protecting its own industry and agriculture sectors from a more developed country or grouping. In this case, consumers will lose because they have to pay higher prices for imports from the rest of the world but allow domestic producers to develop as an "infant industry" (List).

The Common External Tariff in UEMOA is based on 4 rates from 0% to 20%. In ECOWAS, a 5° rate has been recently added at 35%. The CET structure adopted by the UEMOA countries is not really protective of domestic enterprises as it offers less nominal protection to the intermediate and finished consumer's goods in West Africa (for instance, Nigeria bound tariff for agricultural products are at 150% at WTO, while applied tariff are only 33.6%, but Senegal bound tariff are 29.8%, and worse position is for Ivory Coast bound tariff 14.9%).

Economists see prices as contributing to the functioning and stability of food markets. But unlike other markets, food prices affect one of the most fundamental human rights: the Right to Food. The right to food stipulates that each human being has the right to access to means to produce food or to have the income required to buy sufficient food.

Falling food prices, if it leads to rising food imports in the poorest countries generate dislocation of small-scale farmers production which suffer of competition from large-scale producers of developed countries, who are not only infinitely more productive but also heavily subsidized. This competition generates more poverty, losses of jobs, and regional and international migrations.

Ensuring food security and reducing hunger and poverty requires resolute and comprehensive strategies and policies consistent with the right to food.

References

Acts of the Mindelo Conference. 1-6 December 1986. C.I.L.S.S. - Club du Sahel - O.C.D.E. 1987.

Azoulay, G. 2006. «Pour une sécurité alimentaire durable des pays les plus pauvres», in «*Le monde peut-il nourrir le monde? Sécuriser l'alimentation de la planète*» edited by B. Hubert and O. Clément, 133-145, QUAE-IRD Editions.

Azoulay, G. 2012. «Sécurité alimentaire mondiale et crise structurelle d'un mode de fonctionnement de l'économie agricole», in «*La terre, une marchandise? Agriculture et mondialisation capitaliste*». L'Homme et la société, n°183-184: 61-81.

Benin, S., A. Ninn Pratt, S. Wood, and Z. Guo. 2011. "*Trends and Spatial Patterns in Agricultural Productivity in Africa, 1961–2010.*" ReSAKSS Annual Trends and Outlook Report 2011 Washington, DC: IFPRI.

Conference of Ministers of Agriculture of the African Union. 2003. Report of the Ministers of Agriculture (Maputo, Mozambique). Available at: http://www.fao.org/docrep/MEETING/006/AD121E/AD121E00.HTM#P192_22456.

FAO. 2016a. *Cereal Supply and Demand Brief*, 05/05/2016. Available at: http://www.fao.org/worldfoodsituation/csdb/en/.

FAO. 2016b. Food Price Index, 05/05/2016. Available at: http://www.fao.org/worldfoodsituation/foodpricesindex/en/.

Rakotoarisoa M. A., M. Lafrate, and M. Paschali. 2011. "*Why has Africa become a Net Food Importer? Explaining Africa Agricultural and Food Trade Deficits*". Trade and markets division, Food and Agriculture Organization of the United Nations, Rome, 2011.

Fermont, A.M., P.J.A. van Asten, P. Tittonell, M.T. van Wijk, and K.E. Giller. 2009. "Closing the Cassava Yield Gap: An Analysis from Smallholder Farms in East Africa." *Field Crop Res* 112: 24-36.

Frankel, J. 2014. "Why are Commodity Prices Falling?" World Finance. Available at: http://www.worldfinance.com/home/why-are-commodity-prices-falling.

Garrity, D., J. Dixon, and J.M. Boffa. 2012. *Understanding African Farming Systems: Science and Policy Implications*. Prepared for "Food Security in Africa: Bridging Research and Practice". Sydney 29-30 November 2012. Australian Center for International Agricultural Research.

Lipton, M. 1977. *Why Poor People Stay Poor: Urban Bias in World Development*. Cambridge: Harvard University Press.

Otsuka, K., and D. Larson, Eds. 2012. *An African Green Revolution: Finding Ways to Boost Productivity on Small Farms*. Springer Dordrecht.

Pretty, J., C. Toulmin, and S. Williams. 2014. "Sustainable Intensification in African Agriculture." *Annals of Botany* 114: 1571–1596.

Tittonell, P., and K.E. Giller. 2013. "When Yield Gaps are Poverty Traps: The Paradigm of Ecological Intensification in African Smallholder Agriculture." *Field Crop Research* 143: 76-90.

UNDP. 2015. "*Human Development Report 2015* - Work for Human Development", UNDP, Available at: http://report.hdr. undp.org/.

40662079R00099

Made in the USA
Middletown, DE
19 February 2017